VOICES FROM THE NATIONS

We the
Chinese

VOICES FROM THE NATIONS

WE THE CHINESE

CHINESE

Voices from China

Edited by Deirdre and Neale Hunter

PRAEGER PUBLISHERS
New York · Washington · London

PRAEGER PUBLISHERS
111 Fourth Avenue, New York, N.Y. 10003, U.S.A.
5, Cromwell Place, London S.W.7, England

Published in the United States of America in 1971
by Praeger Publishers, Inc.

Fifth printing, 1974

© 1971 by Praeger Publishers, Inc.

Library of Congress Catalog Card Number: 78–83337

Printed in the United States of America

CONTENTS

PART THREE: *The Cultural Revolution*

LIST OF ILLUSTRATIONS

PREFACE

It is high time we stopped thinking of China as mysterious. In the nineteenth century it was the place where those "inscrutable orientals" lived; in the twentieth, after a brief period when it was "our courageous ally" against the Japanese, it has gone back to being an enigma—the "land behind the bamboo curtain."

This attitude is based partly on our own ignorance. In a world armed to the teeth with nuclear weapons, ignorance is no longer tolerable. It is the duty of people who know the truth about China to pass on their knowledge to the general public, and, more importantly, to explain how the man in the street can find out the truth for himself.

In fact, a great deal is known, not only about the land itself but also about the lives its people lead. Although Americans have been discouraged—first by their own government, later by the Chinese—from going to China or trading with her, thousands of visitors from almost every country in the world have gone there as teachers, tourists, delegates, and businessmen, and seen with their own eyes what the society is like. Many have written books about their experiences, and these are useful sources of information.

Then there is the publicity that China gives herself, in the form of magazines, news bulletins, and radio programs in foreign languages. These must be taken with a grain of salt, of course, for every country likes to present itself favorably.

Checked against the conclusions of outside observers, however, Chinese propaganda can be very educational.

A third way of finding out about China is to get hold of some of the intelligence information gathered and published by the American Consulate in Hong Kong. This is available in certain college libraries, as are British monitorings of provincial Chinese radio broadcasts.

A far easier and more satisfactory method—though the one that attracts the least attention of all—is simply to read Chinese literature. Thousands of works by contemporary Chinese writers have been translated into English, but they are completely unknown to the American public. We would laugh at someone who thought he knew all there was to know about France but had never laid eyes on a French novel, play, or poem. Yet, of the very few American schools and colleges that teach the Chinese language or culture, hardly any offer a course in modern Chinese literature. To make matters worse, there are only two or three bookshops in the whole country that import Chinese publications, and these are required by law to insert into each book a warning that the material does not have the blessing of the State Department!

Creative literature, whatever political assumptions it makes, is always revealing. We do not go to it asking for facts. Fiction, by definition, is not factual; every writer invents and embroiders in order to tell his tale. But the reader can often arrive through fiction at a far more profound truth than the data that can be tabulated by a computer or whatever can be gleaned by listening to a country's radio broadcasts or by photographing every square inch of its territory from satellites.

This book is an attempt to make up, in a small way, for the lack of Chinese material available to Americans. It uses both literary and journalistic selections, in an anthology designed not only to show what the Chinese, particularly the young, read and consider important, but also to give an idea of what life is like in China today.

The extracts will seem strange to some readers, who will probably find it hard to identify with their Chinese counterparts. It should be emphasized, therefore, that China is easier to appreciate if three essential facts are kept in mind.

The first is the antiquity of Chinese culture. No other country on earth can look back on such a long history of continuous civilization. This makes China unique; she is not, except in the purely economic sense, a "newly emergent" or "underdeveloped" nation. In comparison with her, it is *we*, the European and New World countries, who are the youngsters of history. Europe conquered the world in the nineteenth century by virtue of a "great leap forward" in military and industrial technology, and we are the heirs to the power and wealth thus acquired. It is perfectly natural for China to want to catch up. She is bound to become what she always was—one of the most powerful, original, and influential countries in the world.

The second point is that China has just emerged from a hundred years of the most humiliating degradation that a proud culture can suffer. Her economy, her system of government, her art and literature, and her religions were shattered by the impact of Western commercial, military, and cultural might. The Chinese have lived through generations of chaos; they have seen their territory occupied, their raw materials taken, their livelihood constantly threatened by famine and war. Before the Communist victory in 1949, it seemed that China's spirit had been broken forever, and the West went into premature mourning for "the sick man of Asia."

The third thing to remember is that China's success in creating a viable society did not happen by chance, nor was it handed to China on a plate. The Chinese people fought tooth and nail for their survival. In the nineteenth century they fought the Europeans; they fought their own foreign rulers, the Manchus; they fought rapacious warlords and landlords; in the 1930's and 1940's they fought back against the Japanese invasion; and finally, in one last great convulsion, they smashed the American-equipped armies of Chiang Kai-shek. The China that emerged in 1949 was a nation born in the flames of war and revolution. And if that seems an inauspicious or somehow illegitimate start for a new society, we should remind ourselves that America began in exactly the same way, and that her "war of national liberation" from British colonialism provided much of the original inspiration for the Chinese struggle.

These three facts are prerequisites for understanding China. People who quibble with them, who say "Ah, but the Chinese are still not free for all that!" or "Yes, but the peasants are still dirt-poor!" merely betray their ignorance of what China has been through. The only way to judge the China of today is to set her alongside the China of yesterday: Are thousands of corpses scraped off the streets of Shanghai every year? Do millions die every decade from famine and flood? Are 90 per cent of the population illiterate? Does the currency drop in value from day to day? Are women the chattels of men? Do the police have to be armed?

These are the kind of questions one should ask. When a student of China can answer them with an emphatic "No!" and feel something of the relief and the pride that the Chinese feel when they answer "No!" to them, then he has begun to understand that the "mystery" of China is in fact a very clear and very moving story of human courage, the rebirth not only of a nation but of one quarter of mankind.

If this book gives even a hint of the significance of this rebirth, it will have been worth the making.

DEIRDRE AND NEALE HUNTER

PART ONE

Moving the Mountains

Schoolgirls

THE FOOLISH OLD MAN WHO REMOVED

THE MOUNTAINS

[People who imagine they don't know the first thing about China probably underestimate themselves. They *do* know one thing, and it could well be the first thing to know—the name Mao Tse-tung.

Mao is justly famous. Few men have led so many people through such momentous times. When history takes stock of the twentieth century, Mao will have as much right to pride of place as anyone. For over fifty years he has been in the vanguard of the fight to set China free—free from itself, from its own chaos, and free from the foreign powers that battened on its misery.

For much of that time he was a hunted man. He lost his wife and several other members of his family to the executioner. To escape Chiang Kai-shek, he led his troops on foot some 7,000 miles, fighting and backtracking much of the way, in a year-long march over militarily impossible terrain. And while the Communists were exiles in their own country, he lived for years in caves in remote mountain bases.

Mao has been Chairman of the Chinese Communist Party since 1935. Under his leadership, Communism grew from a band of guerrillas into a force that neither the Japanese armies nor the millions of men under Chiang Kai-shek could defeat. Since the founding of the People's Republic in 1949, it is Mao who has been the principal architect of the society that has risen from the ashes of old China.

3

Small wonder, then, that the Chinese regard him as a kind of savior and see his writings as the key to their new world, as a gospel of moral and political theory.

Westerners who read Mao often find him heavy going. For the Chinese peasants—and we must continually remind ourselves that four out of five Chinese live on the land—he is not at all hard to fathom. Of rural extraction himself, he seems to have the knack of communicating with the peasants, who like his straightforwardness, his wry humor, his blunt phrases that smell of the farm, and his habit of quoting old proverbs.

He has written everything from classical poetry to essays on Marxist philosophy. But the pieces that the Chinese love best, the ones that almost everyone knows by heart, are the shortest, simplest, and to us least political of his writings. Known in China as "The Three Old Favorites," they are without a doubt the most widely read literature in the world today. It would therefore seem appropriate to begin with one of them—partly because Mao wrote it and partly because few documents could lead us so directly into the heart of our subject.

"The Foolish Old Man Who Removed the Mountains" was written in 1945, just before the end of World War II. At that time, the job ahead of the Communists must have looked endless. The Japanese still occupied large parts of China, and even after they would be driven out, Chiang Kai-shek would still be there—and he was, on paper at least, two or three times stronger than the Communists and had been committed for twenty years to their destruction.

Mao used a 2,000-year-old fable to make his point, which was that the Communists would gain the support of the people only if they cultivated the traditional peasant qualities of persistence and patience, courage and conviction. The "wise" men, the intellectuals with university degrees, might say their chances of success were nil. Well, they would confound these pundits by taking the long view of history, the view of the peasant. And in the process they would win the peasants to their side.

The novelty in Mao's approach was that communist movements before him had tended to despise the peasants as less reliable than the workers in the cities. When Mao wrote: "Our God is none other than the masses of the Chinese people," he was stating his faith in China's illiterate millions, who, he predicted, would eventually form an army of liberation.

History was to fulfill this prophecy in no uncertain way.

Mao begins by summarizing the results of the Seventh National Congress of the Communist Party of China, stressing the need for unity in the long haul ahead. The article continues:]

There is an ancient Chinese fable called "The Foolish Old Man Who Removed the Mountains." It tells of an old man who lived in northern China long, long ago and was known as the Foolish Old Man of North Mountain. His house faced south and beyond his doorway stood the two great peaks, Taihang and Wangwu, obstructing the way. He called his sons, and hoe in hand they began to dig up these mountains with great determination.

Another graybeard, known as the Wise Old Man, saw them and said derisively, "How silly of you to do this! It is quite impossible for you few to dig up these two huge mountains." The Foolish Old Man replied, "When I die, my sons will carry on; when they die, there will be my grandsons, and then their sons and grandsons, and so on to infinity. High as they are, the mountains cannot grow any higher and with every bit we dig, they will be that much lower. Why can't we clear them away?"

Having refuted the Wise Old Man's wrong view, he went on digging every day, unshaken in his conviction. God was

An illustration of *The Foolish Old Man* from an
English-language children's book published in Peking

moved by this, and he sent down two angels, who carried the
mountains away on their backs.

Today, two big mountains lie like a dead weight on the
Chinese people. One is imperialism, the other is feudalism.
The Chinese Communist Party has long made up its mind
to dig them up. We must persevere and work unceasingly,
and we too will touch God's heart. Our God is none other
than the masses of the Chinese people. If they stand up and
dig together with us, why can't these two mountains be
cleared away?

THE WHITE-HAIRED GIRL,

ACT I, SCENE II

[Let us look more closely at the two great stumbling-blocks—feudalism and imperialism—that Mao singles out as the main obstacles to China's progress.

Feudalism, in Chinese Communist usage, refers to the social system of classical China, which lasted from before the time of Christ right down to the early twentieth century.

In essence, this system consisted of the Emperor, or "Son of Heaven," sitting on his throne in the capital, while highly-educated Mandarins, or "scholar-officials," governed the provinces in his name. These super-bureaucrats, who got their jobs only after passing grueling state examinations, were responsible for keeping the peace, collecting taxes, administering justice, and supervising public works.

Democracy was very scarce in this society. The vast majority of the population—the peasants—had little power. They were subject to a complex burden of authority: the officials kept them in their place by combining administrative power with age-old cultural traditions of loyalty and obedience; the landlords, with official support, forced them even further down by economic exploitation. Peasants who had land could barely make a living from it; the landless had to work the landlords' fields and pay for this "privilege" with a substantial part of the crops they raised.

7

In good seasons this system worked despite its injustice. But when times were bad, the peasants had to borrow to pay the rent. Landlords often doubled as moneylenders, increasing their power over the poor. Interest rates were cruel, and debts tended to get worse, not better. When life became intolerable for enough people, there would be an uprising or sometimes a full-scale rebellion. But even when rebel armies managed to overthrow the ruling dynasty, the system itself remained intact and the cycle recommenced under subsequent rulers.

The arrival of the Europeans in the nineteenth century seriously disrupted China's rural economy. Simultaneously, the military defeats inflicted by Western armies aggravated the growing disgust the Chinese felt toward their Manchu rulers. This was the time when many Western ideas—and particularly the whole notion of democracy—began to penetrate Chinese society.

Democratic principles played a big part in the Revolution of 1911, when the entire imperial system was swept away. A Western style of government was set up, but despite the efforts of the revolutionary leader, Sun Yatsen, it proved unworkable. Instead of parliamentary rule, China got a reign of terror, as warlords fought each other for control of the country. This gave the landlord class a new lease on life, and they hung on desperately to their power. Some even hired private armies to defend them from the peasants, millions of whom had reached the end of their endurance.

We in the West have heard a lot about the "wise men" of China, the scholars and landowners with their long silk gowns and wispy white beards and apt quotations from Confucius. We have not yet heard the peasants' version of the story. We have hardly begun to imagine what it was like to live near the verge of starvation, to be forced to sell children into slavery, to have no recourse to courts of higher appeal, to be completely subordinated to the will of a minor despot.

The Chinese knew this side of life very well, but few could agree on the best way to end the injustice. The Communist Party, founded in 1921 by twelve men hiding in a Shanghai girls' school, was only one of many attempts at a solution. At first it dissipated much of its energy by trying to build bases among the urban poor, in the hope of taking over China's key cities and bringing about a revolution in the Russian manner. This concentration of its forces made it highly vulnerable, and Chiang Kai-shek, who had seemed sympathetic for a time, finally turned on the Communists in 1927 and slaughtered many thousands of them.

This and other failures forced the Party to turn to the peasants. Here they found a class whose political understanding might have been rudimentary compared with the city workers, but whose sheer numbers and depth of suffering made them potentially valuable allies. The Communists preached land reform and the overthrow of landlord power and carried these principles into practice in the areas where oppression operated.

Their popularity fluctuated for a time, then grew rapidly when the Japanese invasion began in the 1930's. In many parts of China they became a symbol of "people's power." This prompted something of a renaissance of folk art and literature, as the people began to dramatize their experiences and the new hope they glimpsed for the future.

At Yenan, the Communists' main base against the Japanese, some of these stories became famous. One—"The White-haired Girl"—was particularly successful and has remained a great favorite down to the present. The people liked it because it expressed most clearly the fact they all knew best: the misery of the peasants.

Briefly, the story is as follows: A landlord forces an old peasant to sell his only daughter in lieu of rent. The shock breaks the old man, who kills himself. The girl becomes a servant in the landlord's house, is brutally raped by him, and decides to escape. She goes to the mountains, where she lives on wild vegetables and whatever she can scavenge from temples at night. Her hair turns white from the lack of protein in her diet, and the local people, who catch sight of her occasionally, begin to worship her as "the white-haired goddess." Finally, the Communist Army passes by; the case is investigated and the girl is returned to the village, where she leads the people in confronting the landlord with proof of his crimes.

If the tale seems somewhat melodramatic to us, it certainly moves the Chinese. It symbolizes to them not only the exile of the Communists in their mountain bases, but also the exile of the whole Chinese people from their "promised land" of a just society. Even today, audiences that see "The White-haired Girl" in opera or ballet form readily identify with the heroine and her family, and there are not many dry eyes in the theater after a performance.

The extract that follows is from Act I of the opera. It describes how the girl's father, Old Yang, learns from the landlord that his daughter, Hsi-erh, has been "requisitioned" to pay his debts. Ironically, it is New Year's Eve—a time for rejoicing but also the day when debts had to be settled.]

LANDLORD HUANG's *house. The stage presents the entrance and a small room near the reception hall, furnished with a table and chairs. A candle in a tall candlestick on a table lights up an account book, abacus, inkstone, and old-fashioned Chinese pipe.*

Sounds of laughter, clinking of wine cups, and the shouts of guests playing drinking-games are heard offstage. LANDLORD HUANG *comes in, cheerfully tipsy, picking his teeth.*

HUANG: Well, I haven't lived in vain. I have nearly 250 acres of good land and every year I collect at least 1,000 piculs in rent. All my life I've known how to weight the scales in my own favor and manage things smoothly. These past few years our family has done pretty well. Of course, last year my wife died. But I feel more free without a wife. Women are as cheap as dirt. If one takes my fancy—like this one tonight—it's very easy to arrange.

(Mu, *the* LANDLORD's *secretary, leads on* YANG, *the peasant.*)

MU: Old Yang, Landlord Huang is here. This way.

HUANG (*politely*): So it's Old Yang. Sit down, won't you?

(*He indicates a seat, but* YANG *does not dare to sit down.*)

MU (*pouring tea*): Have some tea.

(YANG *remains silent.*)

HUANG: Have you got everything ready for New Year, Old Yang?

YANG: Well, sir, you know how it is. It's been snowing for more than ten days, and we have no firewood or rice at home. I've not lit the stove for several days.

MU: Look, Old Yang, there's no need to complain about poverty. Landlord Huang knows all about you, doesn't he?

HUANG: Yes, Old Yang, I know you're not well off. But this year is passing, and I'm afraid I have to trouble you for the rent. (*Opens the account book.*) You cultivate one acre of my land. Last year you were five pecks short, this summer another four and a half pecks, in autumn another five and a half pecks.

MU: (*reckoning on the abacus*): Five times five . . . two fives are ten . . .

HUANG: And remember the money you owe us. In my father's time your wife died, and you wanted a coffin, so you borrowed five dollars from us. The year before last you were sick and borrowed two and a half dollars. Last year another three dollars. At that time we agreed on five per cent monthly interest. At compound interest that amounts to—

MU (*reckoning on the abacus*): The interest on the interest amounts to . . . five times five, twenty-five. Two fives are ten . . . Altogether twenty-five dollars and fifty cents. Plus one and a half piculs' rent.

HUANG: Altogether twenty-five dollars and fifty cents, plus one and a half piculs' rent. Right. Old Yang?

YANG: Yes, sir. . . . That's right.

HUANG: See, Old Yang, it's down here quite clearly in black and white, all correct and in order. This is New Year's Eve, Old Yang. The rent must be paid. If you've got it with you, the debt is cancelled. If you haven't got it with you, then go and find some way of raising it. Steward Mu will go with you.

MU: Get going, Old Yang!

YANG: Mr. Mu . . . Sir . . . I have no money. I can't pay the rent or the debt. (*His voice falters.*) Sir . . .

HUANG: Now, Old Yang, that's no way to act. This is New Year's Eve. You're in trouble, but I'm even worse off. You must clear the debt today.

YANG: Sir . . .

HUANG: Come, you must be reasonable. Whatever you say, that debt must be paid.

MU: You heard what Landlord Huang said, Old Yang. He never goes back on his word. You must find a way, Old Yang.

YANG: What can I do? An old man like me, with no relatives or rich friends—where can I get money? (*Beseechingly.*) Sir . . .

HUANG (*seeing his opportunity, signals to* MU): Well . . .

MU (*to* YANG): Well, listen, Old Yang, there is a way. Landlord Huang has thought of a way for you, if you'll take it . . .

YANG: Tell me what it is, Mr. Mu.

MU: You go back, and bring your daughter Hsi-erh here as payment for the rent.

YANG (*horror-stricken*): What!

MU: Go and fetch Hsi-erh here as payment for the rent.

YANG (*going down on his knees*): Sir, you can't do that!

HUANG (*stands up in disgust*): Look, I'm doing you a favor, Old Yang. Bring Hsi-erh to our house to spend a few years in comfort; and won't she be better off than in your place, where she has to go cold and hungry and has such a hard time of it? We won't treat her badly here, and this way your debt will be cancelled too. (*Laughs.*) Isn't that killing two birds with one stone?

YANG: No, sir, you can't do it. . . .

MU: Well, Old Yang, it seems to me that you poor people try to take advantage of the kindness of the rich. Landlord Huang wants to help your family. Just think, Hsi-erh will have the time of her life here. She'll live off the fat of the land, she'll dress like a lady, she'll only have to stretch out her hand for food and drink! In your place she's cold and hungry. In fact, Landlord Huang is quite distressed by all you make her put up with. So you'd better agree.

YANG: But, sir, Mr. Mu, this child Hsi-erh is the apple of my eye. Her mother died when she was three years old, and I brought her up as best I could. I'm an old man now and she's my only daughter. She's daughter and son to me. I can't let her go. . . .

HUANG: I'm not going to wait much longer, Old Yang! Make your choice. Give me the girl or pay your debt.

MU: Old Yang, Landlord Huang is in a good humor now. It'll be worse for you if you offend him.

HUANG (*angrily*): That's enough! Make out a statement! Tell him to send the girl tomorrow! (*He starts to leave.*)

YANG (*stepping forward to clutch at him*): Don't go, sir!

HUANG (*pushing* YANG *aside*): Get away! (*He hurries out.*)

MU: All right, Old Yang, you'd better give in. (*He goes to the table to make out a statement.*)

YANG (*barring his way wildly*): You mustn't . . . you mustn't . . .

MU: Get wise, Old Yang. Don't keep being such a fool.

You've got to agree to this today, whether you like it or not! (*He pushes* YANG *aside and begins to write the statement.*)

YANG (*seizing* MU's *hand*): No!

MU (*furiously*): You must!

YANG (*makes to rush out*): I . . .I'll go somewhere to plead my case!

MU (*shouting*): Where are you going to plead your case? The county magistrate is a friend of ours!

YANG (*trapped*): I . . .

MU: It's no use, Old Yang. You're no match for him. I advise you to let me make out a statement and you put your mark on it and the business is settled. (*He writes.*)

YANG (*stopping him again*): You . . . you . . .

(*Enter* HUANG, *very impatient.*)

HUANG: Why are you so stubborn, Old Yang? Let me tell you, it's going to be done today whatever you say! (*To* MU.) Hurry up and make out that statement.

YANG (*moaning helplessly*): Ah . . .

MU (*reading as he writes*): "Tenant Yang owes Landlord Huang one and a half piculs of grain and twenty-five dollars and fifty cents. Because he is too poor to pay, he wants to sell his daughter Hsi-erh to the landlord to cancel the debt. Both parties agree and will not go back on their word. Since verbal agreements are inconclusive, this statement is drawn up as evidence. . . . Signed by the two parties, Landlord Huang and Tenant Yang, and the witness, Steward Mu. . . ." Right, talk is empty but writing is binding. Come on, Old Yang! Put your mark on it!

YANG (*beside himself*): You can't do this!

HUANG: What? All right, tell Liu to tie him up and take him to the county court!

YANG (*panic-stricken*): No, not the county court!

MU (*seizing* YANG's *hand*): Put your mark on it! (*He presses his fingers down.*)

YANG (*at the sight of the ink on the paper*): Ah! (*He falls to the ground.*)

MU: Aha! One fingerprint has cleared the debt of years. (*He hands the document to* HUANG, *who makes a sign that he should examine* YANG.)

MU (*bending over* YANG): He's all right.

HUANG: Old Yang, you'd better go home now. Bring Hsi-erh here tomorrow. (*To* MU.) Give him the document.

MU (*helping* YANG *up*): Here, this one is yours. Tomorrow send Hsi-erh here to give New Year's greetings to Landlord Huang's family. Tell her to come and spend a happy New Year. Go on. (*He pushes* YANG *out and shuts the door.*)

HUANG: Old Mu, you take a few men there early in the morning. We don't want the old man to go back and decide to ignore the debt and run away. That way we'd lose both the girl and the money.

MU: Right!

HUANG: Another thing. For heaven's sake don't let the word get around. It wouldn't sound well on New Year's Day. If those wretches spread the news, even though we're in the right it wouldn't look good. If anyone asks, just say my mother wants to see Hsi-erh and you're fetching her to pay her New Year's respects.

MU: Good. (*He goes out.*)

HUANG (*to himself*): The only way to get rich is at the expense of the poor. I had to break Old Yang to get his daughter.

(*Curtain*)

THE OPIUM WAR

[After feudalism, the second "mountain lying like a dead weight on the Chinese people" was imperialism.

Many people nowadays, especially in the West, find this word distasteful. It is commonly assumed that the age of empire is a thing of the past, that the days when the white man conquered the world in order to civilize it are over and will never return.

The Chinese have a different interpretation. The way they see it, the West's territorial conquests in the last century were made to ensure a plentiful supply of cheap raw materials for Western industry and also to open up markets for Western products. The extraordinary economic growth of countries like Britain, France, and the United States was facilitated by the exploitation of the unindustrialized world during this crucial period.

China was never fully colonized, though a dozen white nations had carved out spheres of influence, and the so-called unequal treaties gave foreign powers either outright possession of Chinese territory (as in the case of Hong Kong) or economic predominance (as in the treaty ports).

In Chinese eyes, the modern history of China has been —and still is—a fight against encroachment by foreign imperialists. From the first sporadic resistance in the 1840's, through the Boxer Rebellion of 1900, to the life-or-death war against the full-scale Japanese invasion, the Chinese feel they have been fulfilling the sacred duty to defend their land and life-style. The word "imperialism," therefore, does not refer to some abstract political concept but to a process that every Chinese knows is a fact: the attempt by foreign countries to destroy China's territorial, cultural, and economic independence.

In some ways, the Chinese might seem to have won their fight. They have regained control over almost all their former territory—the main exceptions being the island of Taiwan and some disputed border areas. Yet, ironically, they now see themselves surrounded by more brute power, and more deadly forms of power, than they ever had to cope with in the past. They see the United States with almost one million troops to the east and south of them; they see the Soviet Union massing forces to their west and north. China's history has conditioned her to interpret this as a continuation of Western aggression against her.

Perhaps the best way to understand why is to go back and have a look, through Chinese eyes, at the nineteenth century. Here is a piece (from a Chinese history book) that gives the Communist version of the Opium War (1839–42), the first aggressive action against China by Europeans and the one that led inexorably to all that followed.

American readers might be surprised to find that the United States was involved in China's affairs at this early stage. People have a tendency to overlook the unpalatable events of their history. But the fact is that Yankee clipper ships often included opium in cargoes bound for China, and some of Boston's most respectable families engaged in this trade.

The extract is the first chapter of Volume II of *A Short History of China*, written by Lin Yi and published by the Foreign Languages Press, Peking, in 1963. The writer is naturally pro-Chinese, but much of what he says is now admitted by Western historians to be substantially true.]

BANNING THE OPIUM TRADE

The Importing of opium

On the eve of the Opium War, China was still a feudal state. Britain was already the world's foremost colonial power, and her capitalists had been trying for some time to force open China's doors in order to secure markets for their manufactured goods and gain access to her raw materials. The Ching [Manchu] Government, however, closed its doors to such trade. The Chinese people had no use for the cotton and woolen goods that the British merchants were trying to foist on them, their own society being based on a self-sufficient small-peasant economy.

Determined to grab the Chinese market with a view to enslaving and plundering the country, the British *bourgeoisie* persistently tried to sell the poisonous opium to the Chinese people. Increased quantities of opium were sent into China. During the 1830's the opium trade, conducted through the port of Canton, was draining China's treasury by 20 to 30 million taels of silver each year. The price of silver in terms of copper coins increased and on the eve of the Opium War it was twice as costly as during the early Ching Dynasty. The Ching Government insisted that the taxes be calculated in silver. This meant that the peasants, who received only copper coins for their farm produce, had to pay double the previous amount in taxes. The outflow of silver and the devaluation of copper coins in terms of silver depressed the standard of living of the peasant masses, disrupted the finances of the country, and threatened the Ching Government with bankruptcy.

In addition to this financial chaos, opium-smoking caused widespread physical and moral deterioration among the people. According to an 1835 estimate, there were two million opium addicts, including Ching officials both high-ranking and petty, scholars, landlords and gentry, and proprietors and merchants. To the Ching rulers the most disquieting aspect of this widespread opium-smoking was that many of the army officers and men were addicted to the drug. Opium-smoking had sapped their strength and the rulers were dependent upon this force for holding the people in subjection.

While public opinion throughout the country demanded a ban on opium, Emperor Tao Kuang and some Ching officials, alarmed by the menace of the drug, sought a way out of their difficulties. In the ruling circles, however, there were differing views on the question of banning opium. One segment—represented by Lin Tse-hsu, Viceroy of Hunan and Hupeh—was conscious of the ruinous effect of the trade and advocated a thoroughgoing ban. Another segment, larger and more influential, and enjoying the confidence of the Emperor, profited from the trade but openly censured it, while doing everything possible to keep it going. However, under the pressure of public opinion, and with an awareness of the financial and political consequences of the opium trade, Emperor Tao Kuang appointed Lin Tse-hsu, a sterling patriot, as Imperial High Commissioner, and sent him to Canton to ban it.

Banning the opium trade

Lin arrived in Canton in the spring of 1839 and forthwith ordered the foreign merchants to surrender their stocks of opium and sign a bond pledging that, on pain of capital punishment and confiscation of their cargoes, they would not ship any more opium to China.

Captain Charles Elliot, the British superintendent of trade, tried to sabotage the implementation of the order by instructing the British merchants to refuse to hand over the illicit drug or sign a bond. Lin then had his soldiers surround the compounds of the foreign business agents, cutting off their supplies of vegetables and water. He would not allow premises or vessels to be leased to them, and instructed all their Chinese employees to leave.

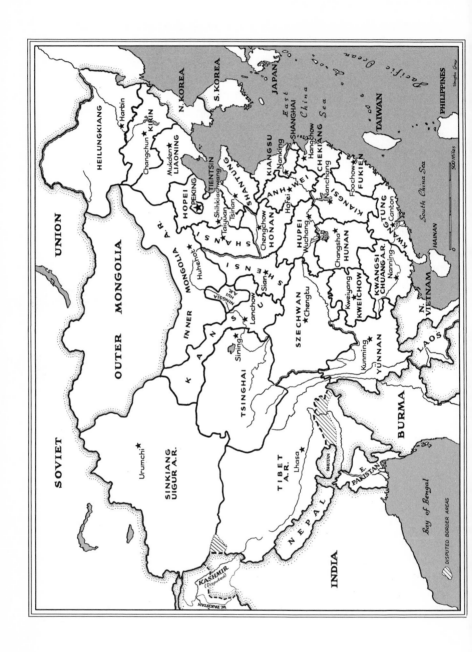

Besieged for three days, Captain Elliot was forced to hand over more than twenty thousand chests of opium, including more than a thousand chests owned by American merchants. On June 3, 1839, Lin set fire to the lot on the beach at the Bogue (Bocca Tigris). The fire lasted twenty days.

June 3, 1839, will go down in Chinese history as the memorable day on which the Chinese people, by direct action, condemned the alien intruders for their crimes. Lin Tse-hsu will long be remembered as the man who, with the support of the people, consummated this righteous deed.

THE OPIUM WAR

British aggression and Ching compromise

The British were determined to reinstitute the vile opium trade, and stepped up aggression against China. They organized an invading force under the command of George Elliot and declared war in April, 1840. The British fleet reached the South China Sea, facing Canton, in June. Finding this port impregnable [Lin Tse-hsu had organized its defense], the invaders turned to Amoy in the province of Fukien, and were again repulsed. The fleet then steamed north and on July 4 attacked Tinghai, an important port in the Choushan Archipelago, off the Chekiang coast. The Chinese troops and civilians put up heroic resistance but were unable to prevent the British occupation of Tinghai, which had been left practically undefended by the Ching Government.

When news of the fall of Tinghai reached Peking, the officials who favored compromise with the British seized the opportunity to discredit Lin Tse-hsu. Emperor Tao Kuang weakened as the British fleet approached Haikou, near Tientsin. He dismissed Lin Tse-hsu and instructed the compromiser Chi Shan to go to Canton and negotiate with the British. The invading fleet then withdrew south to Kwangtung. After George Elliot returned to England because of illness, his office was taken over by the British superintendent of trade, Charles Elliot.

Upon arriving in Canton, Chi Shan dismantled all defense works and disbanded the people's armed forces. The British answered this retreat by a great show of force. In January, 1841, they bombarded and took the forts within the Bogue. They demanded the surrender of a selected part of territory and an indemnity. Chi Shan sent a negotiator to Chuenpi outside the Bogue and concluded the Convention of Chuenpi, which provided for the handing over of Hong Kong and the payment of six million silver dollars to Britain as well as for the opening of Canton to trade.

Emperor Tao Kuang found the terms of the Convention of Chuenpi insulting to his imperial dignity and decided to make a stand in Canton. He appointed Yi Shan to direct the war there. Learning of the Ching Government's plans, the British decided to attack first by advancing on the Bogue forts once again. Admiral Kuan Tien-pei and his men put up a stiff resistance against the invaders and fought heroically to the last man.

In May, 1841, British warships sailed into the Bogue and Yi Shan hoisted the white flag on the city wall of Canton, bringing the war to a temporary halt.

The Ping Ying Tuan (Quell-the-British Corps)

When the British troops reached the outskirts of Canton, they indulged in an orgy of massacring, burning, and looting, thus arousing the bitter hatred of the inhabitants. In May, 1841, when British marauders sneaked into Sanyuanli, near Canton, and started looting, gongs were sounded. Tens of thousands of peasants from over one hundred villages raised banners bearing the emblem "Ping Ying Tuan." Armed with hoes, axes, and pitchforks, they swept down on Sanyuanli and surrounded the looters. The women and children supplied the men with food and water. There was heavy rain and the British soldiers, scurrying about in the muddy fields, got into a panic and were trapped in the bog. Charles Elliot, their captain, ran to the rescue and was surrounded. Despite attempts to break out, more than two hundred British were killed or wounded. Finally Yi Shan sent men to Sanyuanli and persuaded the peasants to disperse. This released Elliot and the remainder of his troops.

The struggle of the Ping Ying Tuan, the first heroic mass fight of the Chinese people in modern history against foreign aggressors, stands out in sharp contrast to the corruption and impotence of the capitulators in the Ching Government.

Britain's second coastal drive

After Yi Shan laid down his arms in Canton on May, 1841, the Ching Government, thinking the war was over, instructed the provincial coast guard command to disband. The avaricious British seized this opportunity and in August invaded China's coast for the second time.

When news of the Convention of Chuenpi reached London in April, 1841, the British Government did not ratify it. Superintendent of Trade Elliot was recalled and Henry Pottinger was dispatched with full powers to launch a large-scale invasion into China. On August 25, British forces under his command made a sudden attack on Amoy and after a fierce battle occupied the city.

A month later, the British attacked Tinghai for the second time. The Chinese defenders made a gallant stand and bloody fighting continued for six days and nights, with heavy casualties being inflicted on the British. Ko Yun-fei, commander at Tinghai, fought to the death, though wounded in forty places. Tinghai finally fell, and Ningpo, a city west of Tinghai, was captured by the British forces on October 13.

Another outstanding commander was Chen Hua-cheng of the Woosung forts. He had risen from the ranks and treated his men well, training them to be brave fighters. When the

British attacked Woosung, in June, 1842, Chen at first held the enemy fleet at bay, crippling some of the ships. But the forts were gradually surrounded by the enemy and Chen's forces were considerably reduced. He received seven wounds and his uniform was soaked in blood, but he stuck to his post. The British gained possession of Woosung only after all the defenders had been killed.

Then, driving westward up the Yangtze, they next occupied Chinkiang in July and pressed towards Nanking. The Ching Government sued for peace.

THE FIRST OF THE UNEQUAL TREATIES

Treaty of Nanking

On August 6, 1842, the British troops, in full battle array, reached the gates of Nanking, ready to attack the city. On August 29, the Ching Government, intimidated by this show of arms, sent representatives to sign a treaty with Britain, aboard an enemy warship anchored off Nanking. This was the infamous Treaty of Nanking, the first unequal treaty signed by China under the influence of aggression by foreign capitalism.

The treaty stipulated that China would open to trade the five ports of Canton, Foochow, Amoy, Ningpo, and Shanghai, that it would cede Hong Kong to Britain, pay an indemnity of 21 million silver dollars, and fix the tariff rates on British goods only after consultation with Britain.

The following year the Ching Government was forced to sign general regulations for trade with Britain at the five ports. It was also compelled to sign the Supplementary Treaty of the Bogue. This treaty established five per cent as the maximum import tariff on British goods; it gave the British permission to lease land and build houses in certain designated areas of the treaty ports; and it gave them "most-favored-nation treatment"—that is, the power to enjoy all privileges conceded by China to any other power—as well as jurisdiction over British subjects in any disputes between Chinese and British merchants. This marked the beginning of extraterritoriality, or consular jurisdiction, in China.

Treaties of Wanghia and Whampoa

The Treaty of Nanking, which gave substantial advantages to the British, made the United States green with envy. In February, 1844, the American Government dispatched Caleb Cushing as its envoy extraordinary to Macao. He demanded that the Ching Emperor grant him an audience in Peking. Reeling from its defeat at the hands of the British, the Ching Government dared not refuse and in July, 1844, signed with Cushing the Treaty of Wanghia, at a village of that name near Macao. This was China's first unequal treaty with the United States. This treaty stipulated that, except for the indemnity and cession of territory, all the privileges granted to Britain should be enjoyed by the United States. In practice, the Treaty of Wanghia went further than the Treaty of Nanking, provided more specific and broader privileges, and placed heavier fetters on the Chinese people. It forced the doors of China wide open for unbridled aggression by the capitalist powers.

Hot on the heels of the United States came the emissary of the French aggressors to levy more blackmail. In October, 1844, the Treaty of Whampoa was forced upon the Ching Government by France.

This treaty provided the French with powers to enjoy all the privileges already accorded to Britain and the United States. In addition, the French were given the power to propagate Roman Catholicism in China. This included permission to erect cathedrals and cemeteries in the five treaty ports. Any Chinese subject found trespassing on these premises was to be handed over to the Chinese local authorities for severe punishment. Thereafter, many missionaries, following closely behind the flow of opium and manufactured goods, streamed into China. In cassocks and surplices, these clerics carried on aggressive activities against China.

Canton people's resistance

When the British demanded entry to Canton, one of the treaty ports, the people, led by the Sheng Ping Sheh Hsueh, campaigned resolutely against them.

This society was an armed mass organization, a local militia for self-defense against the British. It had a membership of several hundred thousand, mostly peasants and handicraftsmen but also merchants and some members of the gentry, in addition to many women.

The tenacious resistance of the people of Canton prevented the British from entering the walled city for many years. In 1849, the British governor of Hong Kong, backed by a powerful army, fought his way up the Pearl River and demanded entry. The Sheng Ping Sheh Hsueh answered this provocative act with the biggest struggle in its history. Under popular pressure, Hsu Kuang-chin, viceroy of Kwangtung and Kwangsi, boarded the British ships in order to reject the demand. He was forcibly detained. As the news of his detention spread, the citizens manned the river banks and prepared to fight. The British then released Hsu Kuang-chin and, temporarily shelving their demands, steamed out of the Pearl River.

Birth of a semicolonial and semifeudal China

The treaties of Nanking, Wanghia, and Whampoa bereft China of her status as an independent country. Step by step, the foreign invaders forced China into the position of a semicolonial, semifeudal country.

The occupation of Hong Kong by Britain at the conclusion of the Treaty of Nanking marked the beginning of the destruction of China's territorial integrity. The foreign aggressors' enjoyment of the "most-favored-nation treatment" and the right of consular jurisdiction also paved the way for further imperialist penetration into China.

The opening of the five treaty ports and the tariff agreement gave the foreigners unlimited opportunity to push the sales of their goods and to grab raw materials. British textiles flooded the Chinese market, penetrated the countryside, and brought ruin to the peasants' cottage industry. The Treaty of Nanking had not put up any barrier against the opium trade, and foreign capitalists continued importing opium into China. Thus silver was drained out of the country and its price rose steadily on the domestic market. In addition, enormous war indemnities had to be paid. This burden was shifted on to the shoulders of the toiling masses, forcing them into bankruptcy and destitution. Under the battering blows of foreign capitalism, China's self-sufficient feudal economy started giving way, and a semicolonial and semifeudal economy began to take shape.

The Chinese people, after the Opium War doubly oppressed by foreign capitalism and domestic feudalism, began to sharpen their spears for action against the foreign aggressors and their own feudal rulers.

LIGHTNING ATTACK ON THE
LUTING BRIDGE

[What were the reasons for the growth of Chinese Communism? Many ingenious arguments have been presented to prove that the Soviet Union was behind it, or that the Japanese invasion provoked it, or that Chiang Kai-shek's blunders allowed it to happen.

The answer that few Westerners care to face squarely is the simplest: that what attracted the Chinese people to Communism was its claim to represent the masses of suffering peasants against the privileged minority of landlords and business interests that oppressed them.

Yet how else are we to explain the unity that the Communists were able to weld among the people, a consciousness of sharing a common poverty and a common destiny that gave their forces—and particularly the Red Army—a spirit that was noticed by everyone who came in contact with it?

The army's spirit was nowhere more in evidence than during the amazing Long March of 1934–35. The Communists themselves are highly conscious of the importance of this epic journey, and their propaganda returns to it again and again as the crux of the story of liberation. Just as the Jews dwell on the Exodus from bondage as the key to their survival as a race, so the Chinese Communists look back to the Long March as the source of their new life and their new spirituality.

It started as a disastrous retreat. Chiang Kai-shek, thinking he had Mao's men trapped in a mountainous region of south-central China, launched several "encirclement campaigns" against them. The Communists, relying on a highly mobile type of guerrilla fighting, as well as the support of the local people in these "liberated areas," turned all the attacks into humiliating defeats for Chiang.

Finally, thousands of concrete pill-boxes were constructed around the Communists, restricting their movements and making it difficult for them to get supplies. Mistakes were also made, by the Communists' own admission, so that they were forced to beat a hasty retreat from the doomed area.

Marching by night, they headed west toward the mountainous country that borders on Tibet. For months they eluded Chiang and his warlord allies, who pursued and harassed them at every turn. After heavy losses and many narrow escapes, they completed a wide swing to the north, crossed the practically uncharted Great Snow Mountains, plodded through hundreds of miles of boggy grasslands inhabited by hostile tribes, and finally reached the country round Yenan in the northwest. Here they were safe, but the cost had been high. Some estimates put their original strength at 200,000 men and the number of survivors at a mere 30,000.

This feat caught the imagination of millions of people, especially in the provinces the Communists passed through. That is why Mao Tse-tung referred to the march as "a manifesto, a propaganda force, a seeding-machine." Organizers were left behind along the way, to build local bases for the dual task of revolution and resistance against Japan.

Part of the Communist success lay in the contrast the Red Army made with Chinese armies before it. Peasants had suffered abysmally at the hands of campaigning soldiers. Their crops had been destroyed, their possessions commandeered, their women raped. The Communists insisted on simple disciplinary rules and punished infractions severely. Red Army soldiers were to pay for everything they used, replace everything they borrowed, never to molest women, and never to treat peasants as anything but members of a family. In this way, they persuaded many people to join them or give them support.

The American journalist Edgar Snow in his book *Red Star over China* has written perhaps the best description of the Long March and the Red Army's spirit that exists in any language. Curiously enough, this book, translated into Chinese and circulated widely in China, was one of the few ways the Chinese people managed to get information about the Communists.

Americans, then, have a readily available account of the Long March at hand. Few people in the West, however, have read Chinese Communist versions of this journey. The one that follows is taken from a collection of eyewitness accounts and was written by Yang Cheng-wu, a regimental commander who played a key role in the Battle of the Luting Bridge. This bridge, which crosses the Tatu River in the mountains of Western Szechuan, was the last chance the Communists had to avoid destruction in a hopelessly remote corner of China. It is not too much to say that China's future literally hung on a chain bridge across a mountain gorge; for, had the Communists not taken the bridge, it is possible that both Mao Tse-tung and his present heir-apparent, Lin Piao, along with thousands of experienced Party members and troops, would have been killed in that valley, and Chinese history as we know it would have been very different.]

A TASK OF HONOR

On May 22, 1935, the First Regiment of the Red Army's First Division made a successful crossing of the Tatu River at Anshunchang. The current was too rapid to permit the building of a bridge there, and it would have taken many days, using the few small boats available as ferries, to transfer our thousands of men to the other side.

A century earlier, the famous general of the Taiping Revo-

lution, Shih Ta-kai, and his army had been annihilated by the
Ching soldiers at Anshunchang. Chiang Kai-shek had dreams
of the Red Army meeting a similar fate. It was necessary to
capture the bridge at Luting—100 miles upstream—and to
cross the river at once to prevent encirclement by the enemy.

This task was given to the vanguard Fourth Regiment, our
west-bank army, by Army Group Commander Lin Piao. The
First Division, which had already crossed the river, would
advance north along the east bank to give support to the
Fourth Regiment by attacking the opposite side of the Luting
Bridge.

THE FIRST DAY OF VICTORY

Early on the morning of May 23, I, with our regiment,
set out from Anshunchang, heading along the west bank
toward the bridge. We had three days to reach it, but the
road twisted like a sheep's guts along the side of the mountains and was full of ups and downs. To our left, the mountains rose vertically into the clouds; their higher slopes were
covered with perpetual snow, which dazzled the eyes and
gave off an intense cold. On our right, dozens of yards below,
were the white-capped waves of the rushing river. One mis-
step could be fatal, but no one worried about the danger. We
had only one thought—to take the Luting Bridge.

We had marched about 10 miles when enemy troops on
the other side of the river began firing at us. We made a 4-
mile detour through the mountains to avoid needless losses.

When we had gone about 20 miles, we came to a large
mountain. Our vanguard ran into a company of enemy
troops and, after a brief, fierce clash, routed them. We
climbed to the summit. On the other side there was a deep,
narrow stream. The enemy had destroyed the bridge over
it, and fording was out of the question. We felled some trees,
built a makeshift bridge, and were soon across.

Cheered by our first victory, we marched with a spring in our step. Then one of our scouts came hurrying back to report, "There's a big hollow in the mountain ahead on the left. It's being held from above by an enemy force about battalion size. They're blocking our advance."

The regimental commander and I led a few men forward at double time to reconnoiter. The mountains rose in sheer cliffs, and there was only a narrow path between them, climbing like a ladder to the sky. Forts had been built at the head of the pass and on the mountain tops.

After careful scouting, we decided to send a party around to the left, to attack the enemy positions from the rear. While one company of the Third Battalion did this, the other two feigned a direct assault. The enemy replied with machine-gun fire and sealed the mouth of the pass. But our men of the First Company succeeded in getting around to the rear, and the other two companies then made a bold frontal attack and drove the enemy from their fortifications. We gave relentless chase, destroying three companies at the foot of the cliff. We captured one battalion commander, one company commander, and two hundred other prisoners.

80 MILES IN 24 HOURS

The next day, the 24th, we had eaten breakfast and were on the road by 5:00 A.M. We had gone only a few miles when we saw a black horse galloping after us. The rider was a messenger from Army Group Headquarters. He handed me a message, then turned and spurred off back the way he had come. The regimental commander and I read the instructions carefully as we walked along. The order read:

> The Military Commission has sent a telegram stating that the west-bank army has until the 25th to take the Luting Bridge. You must march at top speed and do everything in your power to accomplish this glorious mission. In this battle

you will have to break your own regimental record of 53 miles in one day. As you are all war heroes and model Red Army soldiers, we are confident you can fulfill this task. We are preparing to congratulate you on your victory.

The message was signed by Lin Piao himself, the Army Group Commander.

Commander Wang and I looked at each other. "A glorious mission, certainly," I exclaimed, "but a very tough one!"

The 25th was the following day, and we were still 80 miles from the bridge. We would have to cover a two days' march in one. To march on foot 80 miles in 24 hours is a tremendous task, especially when strong enemy resistance can be expected on the way.

It was a race against time. Originally there were two enemy regiments holding the bridge, but we had seen two more brigades hurrying along the other side of the river to reinforce them. Our only hope of victory lay in getting there first. Otherwise it would be almost impossible for the Red Army to cross at Luting.

Because our military and political leaders had no time to stop for a meeting, they had to consult together on the march. It was decided to issue a number of rallying cries: "The Fourth Red Regiment has a glorious battle record. We must complete this mission and maintain our good name!" "Emulate the First Regiment's capture of Anshunchang. Try to match them by taking the Luting Bridge!" At the same time, the deadline for achieving our objective was set at 6:00 A.M. the following morning.

Hurrying to the front of the column, the secretary of the general Party branch and I climbed on a mound and read the order to the men as they marched past. Their pace quickened, and their faces took on a grim and determined look. The shouting of slogans resounded above the roaring of the river and echoed through the hills.

As they marched, groups gathered together, talking enthusiastically. The company Party branch committee and the Party groups were holding a meeting on the run. The men called such discussions "flying meetings."

No sooner had the political work been completed than Menghu Mountain was sighted ahead. This meant a climb of a dozen miles or so, with a similar descent on the other side. It was a dangerous climb, with the Tatu River on the right, towering cliffs on the left, and the narrowest of twisting trails as the path. This was the bottleneck of the road between Anshunchang and the Luting Bridge.

An enemy battalion held the path where it crossed the summit. Fortunately, we crossed at the height of the foggy season. The enemy could not see us clearly and fired wide. We decided to take advantage of the cover provided by the fog and hold our fire. When we got closer, we threw out showers of grenades and used our bayonets. Terrified, the enemy fled. Our vanguard battalion gave chase as far as the village of Mohsimen, where they ran into an enemy battalion and a regimental headquarters unit. Our victorious men plunged in, routed the enemy, and occupied the village.

The enemy had destroyed a bridge over the stream to the east of the village, and it took us two hours to repair it. Then we did 17 miles without a stop. It was evening before we arrived at a little hamlet of ten families on the edge of the Tatu. We still had 37 miles to go to reach Luting.

Suddenly there was a tremendous thunderstorm. The rain poured down. The men had not eaten all day and could not walk as fast as usual. Now their speed was further slowed by slippery mud, and they could not keep up with the pack-animals laden with food and supplies. To make matters worse, as we came down the Menghu Mountain we saw the enemy on the other side of the river, racing neck and neck with us.

The more difficult our problems, the more we had to rally the men and convince them of the need to press on. We called upon all Communists, members of the Youth League, and other enthusiasts to set an example. We told them of the hardships ahead, and stressed the need to reach the Luting Bridge by 6:00 A.M. the next morning. Every man cut himself a staff to help him walk quicker. There was no time to cook a meal, so we ate our rice ration raw, washing it down with cold water.

The challenge roused the men's fighting spirit. But I was worried about the difficulties involved in a 37-mile march on muddy trails in pitch darkness.

Suddenly a few flickering lights appeared on the opposite side of the river. The next moment, they grew into a long string of torches. The enemy troops were making a forced march by torchlight! I immediately conferred with our regimental commander, our chief of staff, and our Party secretary. We decided that we too would carry torches. Should the enemy signal across the river and ask us to identify ourselves, we would pretend we were the three enemy battalions we had already defeated. We directed our bugler to be prepared to sound the calls used by the enemy. Since the enemy troops were all Szechuanese, we picked some Szechuan men from our own ranks and from the prisoners to shout back replies to any questions.

We bought reeds from the folks in the hamlet, made torches, and issued one to each man, with instructions that they were not to be wasted.

Our aim was to cover at least 3 miles per hour. I had a leg wound that was causing me some inconvenience, and the comrades, especially the regimental commander, urged me to continue on horseback. But I decided it was my duty as an officer to set an example. Instead of riding, I issued a challenge, "We will all march together, comrades. Let's see who walks the fastest. Let's see who gets to the Luting Bridge first!"

Taking up the challenge, the men held their torches high and pressed forward.

Torchlight crimsoned the waters of the Tatu. Our lights

and those of the enemy writhed along the river banks like two fiery dragons.

The sharp notes of an enemy bugle rang out, followed by the cry, "Which unit are you?" Our bugler blew the necessary call and our Szechuan men shouted a reply. The enemy was fooled. They never suspected that the gallant Red Army they hoped to wipe out was marching parallel with them.

They stayed with us for almost 10 miles. Around midnight, the rain grew heavier, and the torches on the opposite bank disappeared. We guessed they had found the going too hard and encamped. The news spread quickly through the regiment, causing many comments among the men, "This is our chance! March on! Faster!" In single file, we pushed on for all we were worth.

The rain pelted down mercilessly and the mountain gullies turned into rushing torrents. The twisting path became as slippery as oil, so that our walking staffs were of little use. We could not march; we slipped and slithered, scrambled and crawled along. And when we came to an even stretch, the weary men would doze off as they walked. A soldier would come to a halt and the comrade behind would push him and yell, "Keep going! Keep going!" The man would awaken and hurry to catch up. Finally the men took off their puttees and tied themselves together in a long chain.

In this way we kept up the forced march all night and reached our destination on time. In 24 hours, in addition to fighting and repairing wrecked bridges, we had covered 80 miles. This was truly an exploit of winged feet.

WE WANT THE BRIDGE, NOT ARMS

We first captured the west bank and the western approaches to the Luting Bridge. Having occupied several buildings and a Catholic church, our men prepared for the coming battle. Regimental Commander Wang and I went out with the battalion and company officers to study the situation. We were taken aback by the difficulties to be overcome. The river's reddish waters cascaded down the mountain gorges of the upper reaches and pounded against ugly boulders in midstream, tossing white foam high into the air. The roar of the rushing water was deafening. Fording or crossing in boats was out of the question.

We examined the bridge. It was made of iron chains, thirteen in number, each link as thick as a rice bowl. Two chains on each side served as hand railings; the other nine formed a catwalk. Planks had originally been laid across these, but they had been taken by the enemy, leaving only the black chains hanging in mid-air.

At the head of the bridge, on a stone slab, two lines from a poem were inscribed:

> Towering mountains flank the Luting Bridge,
> Their summits rise a hundred miles into the clouds.

The city of Luting lay directly beyond the eastern end of

The Luting Bridge

the bridge. It was built half along the shore and half on the mountain slope, and was surrounded by a wall over 20 feet high. The west gate of this wall was just past the end of the bridge. The city was garrisoned by two enemy regiments, and strong fortifications had been built along the mountainside. Machine-gun emplacements close to the bridge kept us under continual fire, and mortar shells rained down on us.

The enemy was confident that this position was impregnable. "Let's see you fly across!" they yelled. "We'll give up our arms if you can do it!"

Our soldiers shouted back: "We don't want your arms. We want your bridge!"

Back from our reconnaisance, we first positioned a battalion to cover the path on the other side of the river. That was the only way enemy reinforcements could come. Then we went round our companies to begin the battle rallies. Morale was high. Each company submitted a list of volunteers for an assault party, and each wanted to be given the honor of taking the bridge.

All the regimental officers met in the church at noon to select a shock force. Discussion had just started when enemy mortar shells blew a gaping hole in the roof of the building. Shrapnel and bits of broken tile showered down on us, but not a man moved.

"The enemy is urging us on," I said. "We must push across this bridge immediately. We must now decide which company will handle the assault."

Liao Ta-chu, commander of the Second Company, jumped to his feet. Usually a taciturn man, he forced himself to speak. His dark, sun-burned face flushed with the effort, and his short, wiry frame trembled with excitement as he said:

"The First Company have already been commended as a Model Company for their part in fording the Wukiang River. It's our turn now. We want to emulate them and win the title of Heroes' Company by taking this Luting Bridge."

"You've got to give the assault mission to us," Wang Yu-tsai, the quick-tempered commander of the Third Company, interrupted, sputtering like a machine-gun. "The Third Company has done well in every battle. We guarantee we will take this bridge!" Somewhat plaintively he added "If we don't get this job, I daren't go back and face my men."

A heated debate followed, with no company willing to yield to another. It was left to the leaders to decide. Commander Wang and I talked it over and finally chose the Second Company to lead the assault. I then rose and said:

"If it's fighting you want, you'll each get your chance. But it's the Second Company's turn to lead off. Now, the assault party will be formed of twenty-two men—Communist Party members and other men known for their bravery. It will be led by Company Commander Liao. This seems a good plan to me. What do the rest of you think?"

The response was a burst of applause from everyone. Commander Liao jumped for joy. Only the commander of the Third Company bent his head and kept grumbling. I tried to reassure him: "The Third Company's job is not easy. You have to go across after the Second Company and lay planks on those chains so that the rest of the men can charge the city. Does that satisfy you?" He smiled.

Men fight better on a full stomach, so I instructed the company commanders to see that everyone was well fed. After the meeting, the secretary of the general Party branch went to the Second Company to prepare for the assault.

The attack began at four o'clock in the afternoon. The regimental commander and I directed it from the west end of the bridge. The buglers gathered together to sound the charge, and we opened up with every weapon we had. The sound of the bugles, the firing, and the shouts of the men reverberated through the valley.

Then the twenty-two heroes, led by Commander Liao, climbed out across the swaying chains in the teeth of intense enemy fire. Each man carried a tommy gun, a broadsword, and twelve hand grenades. Behind them came the officers and men of the Third Company, each carrying a heavy plank as well as full battle gear. They fought and laid planks at the same time.

Just as the assault force reached the eastern bridgehead, huge flames sprang into the sky outside the city gate. The enemy was trying to throw a wall of fire across our path. The blaze licked fiercely around the end of the bridge.

The outcome of the attack was hanging by a hair. The assault squad hesitated for a few seconds, then plunged boldly into the flames. Commander Liao's cap caught fire, but he threw it away and fought on. The others also dashed through the flames and smashed their way into the city. In the street fighting that followed, the enemy brought their full weight to bear against our gallant force. Our men fought until all their ammunition was spent. There was a critical pause as the Third Company came charging to their rescue. Then Regimental Commander Wang and I sped across the bridge with our reinforcements and entered the city.

In two hours, we had destroyed over half of the enemy's two regiments, and the remainder broke ranks and scattered. By dusk we had completely occupied the city of Luting and were in control of the bridge.

Our main task now was to guard against an enemy counter-attack. We knew they had a couple of regiments some 20 miles to the northwest, so we sent one battalion in that direction to act as an outpost guard. We sent another battalion south along the riverbank to hold off the two brigades hurrying toward the bridge.

At about ten o'clock in the evening we heard firing to the south. Assuming the enemy reinforcements had arrived, we prepared for a bitter battle. Then news came that a wounded member of our First Division's Third Regiment had been found. Our First Division had arrived! We could relax.

The First Division had caught up with the enemy 20 miles

south of Luting and a battle had followed. The enemy, afraid of being caught between our two forces, panicked and fled.

We at once dispatched men to meet Chief of the General Staff Liu Po-ch'eng and Political Commissar Nieh Jung-chen. When they reached the city, there was a very happy reunion. Although it was 2:00 A.M., the commanders insisted on inspecting the bridge. Carrying a lantern, I accompanied them across. General Liu examined every detail of the iron chains as if he were trying to memorize the entire bridge. On the way back he stopped in the middle and leaned over the side chains to look down on the turbulent waters of the Tatu below. Tapping his foot on the boards, he murmured, "We've spent plenty of blood and energy to get you, Luting Bridge, but we've got you!"

Among the captured enemy documents, we found an urgent directive from the Szechuan warlord Liu Wen-hui. It stated that the Communists had been trapped, as Shih Ta-kai of the Taipings was trapped, between the Tatu River and the Upper Yangtze. Now was the time to annihilate us.

This was a pipe dream, for although we followed the same route as Shih Ta-kai, history did not repeat itself. Ours was a people's army, led by the Communist Party and Chairman Mao.

The following day, Commander Lin Piao marched up with our main force. His warm congratulations were a great encouragement to us. Then Chairman Mao arrived, and thousands of our troops marched across the Luting Bridge. We had conquered the seething barrier of the Tatu River.

THE WHITE-HAIRED GIRL,

ACT V

[Some Chinese Communist terms give Western readers a lot of trouble. One is the word "liberation." Despite its almost universal use in China, Westerners tend to be skeptical about its accuracy; they prefer to see it between sarcastic quotation marks, implying that the Communist takeover of a country cannot possibly mean the true liberation of its people.

Whatever justification there might be for this view with reference to Europe, it is misleading when applied to China. To the Chinese—and we must again remind ourselves that they are overwhelmingly a peasant people—"liberation" is an apt word to describe the process by which they broke free from oppression. This oppression was not something that existed only in the imagination of the Communists. Nor was it a temporary state brought on by the Japanese invasion. It was an age-old bondage—to debt, for example, which kept whole families wretched for generations; to hunger; to degradation; to ignorance. Liberation was the end of landlord power, freedom from subservience to a privileged class, the beginning of hope and pride and people's power.

In Chinese, the word "liberation" does not have the overtones of "liberty" and "liberalism" that it has for us. The Chinese characters used for this word mean "dissolving away an obstruction and letting a pent-up thrust take its natural course." This is much more in line with Mao

42

Tse-tung's image of mountainous burdens being removed from the backs of the people, enabling them to stand up and live.

In other words, we are not dealing with the sophisticated kind of liberty envisioned in the American Constitution or the Bill of Rights, but with the most rudimentary freedom there is: the freedom to exist as a human being.

For most Chinese, this freedom revolves around the right to make a living from the land. At various times there have been other factors—the right to be free from foreign invasion or bad government or financial chaos—but the basic demand has always been for land.

It is therefore to the Communist land-reform period that we should turn if we are to understand the full significance of the term "liberation." Let us go back then to the story of *The White-haired Girl*, to the final act in this morality play of death and resurrection. Few depictions capture so well the relief of the peasants in the moment of truth, their joy at the prospect of an end to their agony, and, on the other hand, their violent hatred of the landlords, their hunger not only for justice but also for vengeance.

When the extract opens, the White-haired Girl is still in her mountain cave. The Communists have arrived in the area and been told of a "goddess" who "haunts" the local temple. The District Head, or Communist Party representative, together with Ta-chun (the White-haired Girl's fiancé) and several other peasants, are planning to get to the bottom of the mystery.]

Scene I: *The village.*

DISTRICT HEAD: This White-haired Goddess, friends, what miracles has she worked?
TA-CHUN: Yes, what?

OLD MAN: District Head, Ta-chun . . . (*Sings.*)
> The White-haired Goddess often shows herself,
> It's three whole years now we've been seeing her.

FIRST PEASANT (*sings*):
> All of us have seen her,
> She comes and goes without a trace. . . .

SECOND PEASANT: She's all in white! A flash—and she's gone!
(*Sings.*)
> She often appears in the dead of night
> At the Temple of the Goddess!

THIRD PEASANT (*sings*):
> The sacrifice set out one day
> Will be gone by morning!

FOURTH PEASANT (*sings*):
> She utters truths in the temple,
> Every word distinct!

FIFTH PEASANT: It's true. She said— (*Sings.*)
> So long as men are sinful creatures
> We shall have no peace.

SIXTH PEASANT: Steward Mu told us— (*Sings.*)
> The White-haired Goddess is powerful,
> We must mend our ways.

ALL (*sing*):
> If we offend her,
> It will be the end of us!

A YOUNG MAN: That's a pack of lies! Where is this White-haired Goddess? Why haven't I seen her?

(*The crowd is indignant.*)

FIRST PEASANT: How can you say that?

SECOND PEASANT: Everybody knows how powerful the goddess is.

THIRD PEASANT: Who will withstand her wrath if you offend her?

DISTRICT HEAD (*intervening*): Friends, I promise you we'll look into this business of the goddess. In the meantime, if you want to burn incense to her, that's all right. We won't stop you.

OLD MAN: Thank you, District Head.

THE VILLAGERS: Thank you. Thank you. (*They leave.*)

DISTRICT HEAD (*in a low voice*): This is no simple matter. . . .

TA-CHUN: Right. I wouldn't mind betting Landlord Huang is involved. We must solve this mystery. . . . Tonight there'll be a full moon. I think Ta-so and I should go to this temple. . . .

(*They confer in whispers.*)

DISTRICT HEAD: A good idea.

TA-SO: We'll see what happens tonight.

DISTRICT HEAD: Better be on your guard, though.

TA-CHUN: Of course. But I have a feeling our day of vengeance is here.

TA-SO: Let's go and get ready for tonight. (*They walk briskly out.*)

(Curtain)

Scene II: *Evening. The Goddess' Temple. There are offerings on the altar. It is dark and eery.*

Enter TA-CHUN, *carrying a pistol, and* TA-SO, *with an unlighted torch and a knife. They approach the temple door cautiously. After whispering together, they enter.* TA-CHUN *points to a corner and they hide themselves. The wind roars. The temple lamp sheds a weird light. There is a pause.* TA-CHUN *peers out from the gloom, then shrinks back into the shadows. There is musical accompaniment throughout.*

TA-SO (*nervously*): Ta-chun! Ta-chun!

TA-CHUN: Shh! Quiet! (*They fall silent again.*)

(*The* "White-haired Goddess" *enters from outside. She darts behind the altar. After waiting to make sure there is no one there, she comes out to collect the sacrificial offerings.* TA-CHUN *and* TA-SO *leap out from the darkness.*)

TA-CHUN (*shouting*): Who are you?

HSI-ERH (*shrieks in surprise and rushes at* TA-CHUN): Aaaah! (TA-CHUN *fires his pistol and hits her in the arm. She falls, but gets up quickly and runs from the temple.*)

TA-CHUN: After her! Quick!

(*The scene changes to a mountain path.* HSI-ERH, *clutching her wounded arm, is running with difficulty. She jumps over a small stream and disappears.*)

TA-SO: Where's she gone? She's vanished!

TA-CHUN (*peering at the ground*): The trail of blood ends here.

TA-SO (*looking down into the distance*): There's a valley below us. We must have come a long way.

TA-CHUN (*pointing*): Look, Ta-so! There's a glimmer of light!

TA-SO: It must be a cave!

TA-CHUN: Light the torch, Ta-so! (*They jump across the stream and disappear.*)

(*The music continues. One hears the sound of the wind.*)

(*The scene changes again. Inside a cave. An oil-lamp gleams on a ledge of rock, its flickering light revealing the gloom and horror of the scene. Firewood, wild fruit, maize, and temple offerings are piled up to one side.* HSI-ERH, *panic-stricken, crawls in through the entrance, which she then seals with a large rock. Outside,* TA-CHUN's *voice is heard, saying "Ta-so! Here! Here!" The rock moves, then crashes down. The two men enter the cave,* TA-SO *holding the burning torch.* HSI-ERH *dodges aside.*)

TA-CHUN (*covering her with his pistol*): Are you a human being or are you a spirit? Speak!

TA-SO: Quickly! Human being or spirit?

TA-CHUN: Speak or I'll shoot!

HSI-ERH (*snarling with hatred*): I . . .

TA-CHUN: Speak! Speak, and I won't harm you!

HSI-ERH: I . . . I . . . (*Explosively.*) I'm human, human, human!

TA-CHUN: Where are you from?

HSI-ERH (*unused to speaking*): Yang . . . Yangko Village.

TA-SO: Then how did you get here?

HSI-ERH (*ferociously*): Your Huang family! (*Sings.*)
    You hounded my father to his death!
    You drove my beloved Ta-chun away!
    You have done your best to kill me,
    But I will not die!
    I have lived for three years in this cave,
    I have cut a mark on the stone each day,
    Those marks cannot express my grief,
    Only the hatred cut in my bones,
    Only the burning revenge cut in my heart!
    You thought I was dead?
    You were wrong! You were wrong! (*Laughs wildly.*)
    I'm a fire you will never put out!
    I'm a tree you will never root up!

TA-CHUN and TA-SO (*amazed*): What is your name?

HSI-ERH (*sings*):
    I'm the fire in the waste,
    I'm the tree on the hill,
    I am Hsi-erh,
    And I am alive!

(*As* TA-CHUN *and* TA-SO *stand in utter astonishment,* HSI-ERH *suddenly rushes at them, screaming.*)

HSI-ERH: Now that you've come for me, I'll have it out with you! I'll have it out with you!

(TA-SO's *torch is still burning. As* HSI-ERH *gets closer, she recognizes in its light the face of* TA-CHUN, *and stops, paralyzed.*)

HSI-ERH: You? . . . You? . . . Is it you, Ta-chun?

(*She drops to the ground in a faint.* TA-CHUN *and* TA-SO *quickly bend over her.*)

TA-CHUN (*as if in a dream*): It is her. . . . It is Hsi-erh. . . .
(*At a loss for a while, he takes a piece of toweling and begins to bind up her wounded arm, calling to her sadly and softly*). Hsi-erh! . . . Hsi-erh! . . .
(*The pain of the wound brings* HSI-ERH *to herself. She sighs and opens her eyes. Seeing* TA-CHUN, *she relaxes a little, closing her eyes again. There is musical accompaniment.*)
    (TA-CHUN *raises his eyes from* HSI-ERH *and lets them wander around the cave, taking everything in. As he remembers all the past, his tears flow. Then his expression changes. He grows angry.*)

TA-CHUN: Now I understand many things. Ta-so! Go back and report this to the District Head! Have Landlord Huang arrested at once!

TA-SO: Right! (*He hurries off.*)

TA-CHUN (*bending over* HSI-ERH): Hsi-erh! Hsi-erh! It's time to go back.

HSI-ERH (*coming to*): Back? . . . No, I'll never go back.

TA-CHUN: Times have changed, Hsi-erh. More than you can imagine. You remember the Red Army Uncle Chao used to talk about? Well, that Red Army's come. It's here, and the poor have become the masters overnight! It's time for revenge.

HSI-ERH: Revenge . . .

(TA-CHUN *takes off his jacket and slips it over* HSI-ERH's *shoulders. He leads her slowly from the cave. Outside dawn is breaking, and the sound of birds can be heard. Offstage the villagers, on their way to greet* HSI-ERH, *sing as they walk.*)

VILLAGERS:
    The sun is up! The sun is up!
    The sun is a blaze of light!
    We who have suffered for generations
    Are today witnesses to the sunrise,
    And to the defeat of darkness.
    Where is Hsi-erh?

Where is Hsi-erh?
We will tear down the mountains,
We will rip open the caves,
To rescue her!
(TA-SO *leads the* DISTRICT HEAD, AUNTY WANG, AUNTY
CHANG, OLD CHAO, *and others along the path.*)
ALL (*sing*):
Where is Hsi-erh?
TA-SO: There! Look!
(*The people are dumbfounded by* HSI-ERH's *changed appear-
ance. They go up to her one after the other.*)
AUNTY WANG: Hsi-erh!
AUNTY CHANG: Hsi-erh!
OLD CHAO: Hsi-erh!
(*Seeing these familiar faces,* HSI-ERH *is at first unable to
speak. Then she calls their names, falls into* AUNTY WANG's
arms and sobs bitterly. They comfort her.)
DISTRICT HEAD: Friends, this is not a time for sadness. We've
found Hsi-erh. Tomorrow we'll hold a mass meeting and
confront Landlord Huang. She will be avenged.
ALL (*sing*):
Country folk, comrades, don't shed tears!
The old life turned people into ghosts,
But the new life turns ghosts back to people!
Our sister has been saved,
Restored to life,
Restored to us!
(*Singing, they help* HSI-ERH *off.*)
(*Curtain*)

Scene III: *The following morning at sunrise. The gate of the
Huang family ancestral hall, chosen as the place for the
peasants' mass meeting. Gongs sound offstage. Shouts of
"Come to the meeting!" "The meeting is at the Huang ancestral hall!" are heard. Singing begins.*)

The injustice of the ages will be revenged,

The wrongs of a thousand years will be set right!
Hsi-erh, who was made a ghost,
Will be returned to human life today!
Blighted lives will be healed,
The poor will stand up and take power!
Landlord Huang, you have sucked our blood,
You have drunk our sweat,
You have stolen our grain!
Landlord Huang, you have deceived and oppressed us,
You have killed our brothers and sisters!
But today we shall settle the old scores with you!
Today all the old scores will be settled!

(*The curtain rises. Innumerable peasants have stood up to accuse* LANDLORD HUANG. *The* DISTRICT HEAD, TA-CHUN, UNCLE CHAO, *and others are standing on the platform. Self-defense guards, armed with red-tasseled lances and swords, surround the meeting place.* LANDLORD HUANG *stands with bowed head below the platform, while* STEWARD MU *cringes like an animal beside him.* HUANG *has just spoken, and now it is the turn of the people to question him. Feelings are running high.*)

FIRST PEASANT (*sings*):
Landlord Huang, your day is over!
SECOND PEASANT (*sings*):
The day you could hound us to death!
THIRD PEASANT (*sings*):
Squeeze money and grain from us!
FOURTH PEASANT (*sings*):
Take our families from us!
FIFTH PEASANT (*sings*):
Bring tragedy after tragedy upon us
And go unpunished!
ALL (*in chorus*):
Speak, Landlord Huang! Speak up! Speak up!

(LANDLORD HUANG *mumbles, trying to justify himself. The*
crowd grows angry.)
ALL (*in chorus*):
    We warn you, Landlord Huang,
    You have had your day!
    We are in power now,
    The world is ours!
    The time has come for murderers to atone!
    You must pay us the blood debt you owe us:
    Your blood for ours!
(*Two peasant women rush forward.*)
FIRST WOMAN (*sings*):
    You came to us for rent,
    You beat my son to within an inch of his life!
SECOND WOMAN (*sings*):
    You came to us for a debt,
    You broke my father's legs!
ALL (*in chorus*):
    Murderers must atone!
    Pay the blood debt you owe:
    Your blood for ours!
(*Two peasant men rush up.*)
FIRST MAN (*sings*):
    You killed my son!
    You made him repair a dike when the river was flooding.
    My son drowned!
SECOND MAN (*sings*):
    You killed my brother!
    You put him to work building a high tower.
    He fell to his death!
ALL (*in chorus*):
    Murderers must atone!
    Pay the blood debt you owe:
    Your blood for ours!

(*The crowd roars* "Make him speak! Make him answer!"
But LANDLORD HUANG *keeps trying to make excuses.*)

OLD CHAO (*loudly*): Neighbors! Let's not waste our breath
trying to make him confess! Just bring Hsi-erh here!

ALL: Bring Hsi-erh! Bring Hsi-erh! (LANDLORD HUANG *and*
STEWARD MU *cringe noticeably.*)

PEASANT WOMEN (*keening tearfully*):
Hsi-erh . . .

ANOTHER GROUP OF WOMEN (*sing*):
Hsi-erh . . .

ALL (*in chorus*):
Hsi-erh . . . Hsi-erh . . .

ONE PEASANT WOMAN (*sings*):
How this child suffered. . . .
But we will suffer no longer!

ALL (*in chorus*):
We will suffer no longer!
We will have a new life!
The world is ours!
Revenge is ours!
We'll accuse! We'll accuse!
We'll avenge Hsi-erh!

(*As* HSI-ERH *enters, the crowd shouts* "Avenge Hsi-erh!
Avenge Hsi-erh!" *When* HSI-ERH *sees her tormentor,* LAND-
LORD HUANG, *she flies across the stage like a mad thing to
tear out his eyes. But her thirst for vengeance is too much
for her, and she collapses before she reaches him. Her friends
and relations go to her and lift her gently.*)

OLD CHAO (*weeping*): Hsi-erh, child, take all the time you
want. It's your turn to speak.

TA-CHUN: Hsi-erh, do you hear? It's your turn to speak.

HSI-ERH (*as if in a dream*): My turn . . . to speak?

ALL (*thunderously*): Your turn to speak!

AUNTY WANG and AUNTY CHANG: Speak, child!

HSI-ERH: I—will—speak. . . . I will speak! (*Sings.*)

A performance of *The White-haired Girl*
before a village audience

I demand vengeance for what has happened to me,
But there is too much to tell,
A mountain of wrongs!
A sea of evil!
Landlord Huang—
Death by a thousand cuts
Would be too good for you!
ALL (*sing*):
 Death by a thousand cuts
 Would be too good for him!
HSI-ERH (*sings*):
 That year— (*Her voice falters.*)
AUNTY WANG (*sings*):
 That New Year's Eve,
HSI-ERH (*sings*):
 Thick snow falling,
 We were cold, we were hungry—
AUNTY WANG (*sings*):
 They demanded their rent,
 Their pound of flesh!
HSI-ERH (*sings*):
 They killed my father!

They hounded him to death!

AUNTY WANG (*sings*):

Old Yang was hounded to death!

ALL (*sing*):

Too many people
Were hounded to death!
Too many to count!

HSI-ERH (*sings*):

On New Year's Day—

AUNTY CHANG (*sings*):

They took her to Huang's house that day—

HSI-ERH (*sings*):

I could not describe
How I was treated there—

AUNTY CHANG (*sings*):

She was raped!
Raped by Landlord Huang!

(*There is a gasp of shocked disgust from the peasant women.*)

AUNTY CHANG (*sings*):

And then they were going to sell her—

HSI-ERH (*sings*):

As a prostitute!
Landlord Huang—
You are a murderer and a beast!

ALL (*sing*):

Murderer!
Man-eating beast!
Your day of reckoning has come!

(*Unable to control their anger any longer, they rush forward to beat* HUANG. *But the* DISTRICT HEAD *and some others restrain them.*)

DISTRICT HEAD: Wait! Let Hsi-erh finish!

HSI-ERH (*sings*):

With the help of Aunty Chang, I escaped.

It was dark, pitch dark,
I had no idea where I was.
I found a cave in the mountains,
Away from people, away from the sun.
I lived on wild fruit and temple offerings,
Half-ghost, half-human.
I swore,
Though stones might rot and streams dry up,
I would not die!
I would bear my suffering
Until the dawn of vengeance!

PEASANT WOMEN (*sing*):
Now that there is sun,
She will be avenged!

ALL (*sing*):
Now that there is sun,
She will be avenged!

(*The crowd rushes forward and begins to beat* HUANG *and* MU. *The* DISTRICT HEAD *and other cadres try to stop the* people. *The* DISTRICT HEAD *climbs on a table and shouts.*)

DISTRICT HEAD: Friends! I am the government representative here. I support your charges against Landlord Huang, and I agree that Hsi-erh should be avenged! But first we must arrest Huang and Mu for a public trial according to proper legal procedure.

(*The crowd cheers excitedly. Self-defense guards bind* HUANG *and* MU.)

ALL (*sing*):
Landlord Huang, you do well to bow your head!
You do well to tremble with fear!
For today we are cutting free from the old society!
Today we are smashing our chains!

(*The song is repeated as the sun rises higher. Bright sunshine bathes* HSI-ERH *and the surging crowd, who are wild with joy.*)

ALL (*sing*):
  We who have suffered so bitterly in the past
  Shall be our own masters from now on!
  We shall be our own masters from now on!
  Our—own—masters—from—now—on!

(LANDLORD HUANG *crouches before the crowd like a felled tree. The peasants stand proudly in the sunlight, countless arms raised high.*)
                    (*Curtain*)

MARRIAGE

[With the next story, we emerge from the "bitter past"—
as the Chinese call it—into a very different kind of society. It is 1952. The Communists have been in power
for only three years, but in that short time irrevocable
changes have taken place. Of these, the breaking of the
landlords' power has undoubtedly been the most important; and this, by releasing the mechanism that held the
old system together, has affected many related areas.

This story deals with one of these: the tradition of arranged marriages. For many centuries, young Chinese
had virtually no choice in their own marriage. This was
normally arranged by the families concerned, with an eye
not so much to the compatibility of the couple as to the
power and prestige of the families.

The Communists were able to outlaw this custom very
quickly. As with many of their reforms, the idea was not
new. It had been on the Chinese program for half a century. But China had been divided for much of that time,
so that it was only with the reunification of the country
under a single government that a good marriage law
could be enforced.

"Marriage," a short story that appeared in *Chinese Literature* magazine in 1953, tells of the effects of the new
law on young people in the countryside. As a piece of
literature, it is typical of modern Chinese writing. It is
primarily about *people*—well-drawn peasant characters
whose lives would be immediately familiar to the average
reader. It is also a kind of fable, a story with a moral. In

this sense, it is not realistic art; it idealizes the peasants, particularly the young hero and heroine, in order to make a social point, to get across the message that the Marriage Law is good. In other words, though it is a real story, about a truly human situation, it is also part of a campaign to make the new law acceptable to the people.

"Marriage" is in many ways a continuation of *The White-haired Girl*. The same struggle between social classes goes on. The difference is that Landlord Huang had total power over the White-haired Girl, whereas Whiskers Li, the villain of this piece, cannot stop the young people from going their own way. In his paternalistic efforts to arrange a marriage, he represents the dead hand of the past, but he is a pale shadow of his predecessors, for the hero and heroine now have government support in their fight against him.

The lovers—and this is as close to a love story as you get in modern Chinese literature—symbolize the birth of a new generation. In a way, they are also a new breed of people—an interesting blend of strong will and independent thought on the one hand, and unselfishness and community spirit on the other. Some of their qualities are thoroughly Western—the way they put their love before the wishes of their elders, for example. But the love itself is not the passionate Western type; it begins with mutual admiration and grows gradually as the two work together in the community.

The background to the story is typically Chinese. The extended family—aunts, uncles, cousins, and the rest—plays a far greater role than it would in a Western story. Even today, the Chinese are more family-oriented than we are, and conflicts arising between loyalty to relatives and loyalty to the community provide many of the plots in literature.

Furthermore, everyone in the story is a peasant. Life is unsophisticated and slow; the people's problems are such things as raising crops, controlling insects, transporting grain. They use oxen, not tractors; they carry their drinking water from the well; they make their own shoes; they light their houses with paraffin lamps.

The mentality of the characters is also rural. Everyone in the village knows everyone else's business, and their lives intertwine more intimately than those of people in industrial countries. When a family quarrel starts, half the village comes to help settle it. It is a long time since Americans have been writing this kind of story, so that "Marriage" has a quaint, old-fashioned ring about it.]

The drizzle had continued for two or three days, sometimes heavy, sometimes light, but always enough to keep the villagers away from the fields. And they were getting impatient.

Lien-niu made use of the rainy days to make a pair of shoes.

When the morning sun peeped through the clouds, everything looked brighter after the rain, gladdening and refreshing the hearts of men and women.

Lien-niu sat on a low chair in the middle of the room, fondling the pair of shoes. They were well made. She thought to herself, "When he goes to work in the fields again, he'll have something to wear on his feet." The image of a sturdy young fellow took shape in her mind: he was wearing the strong shoes, striding along with his head held high, a figure of unusual dignity. A smile began to play around the corners of her mouth. But hardly had it appeared when she bit her lower lip. As though afraid someone might read her secret, she instinctively cast a glance at her mother—Mother Yuan as everyone called her—in the room at the end of the house. She was startled to see her washing the water jar, a sign that it was time to cook the midday meal. Hastily she popped the shoes into her work basket and shook off the snippets of thread that clung to her blue cotton dress.

"I was going to fetch the water when I'd finished the shoes," she called.

"It's terribly muddy outside," said Mother Yuan. "Just a couple of buckets will do to go on with."

"All right." Lien-niu pulled on her rubber boots and swung the pole with the water buckets over her shoulder. Tossing back her long plaits tied with blue ribbons, she set off.

As she came to the corner of the wall, a tall young man with high cheekbones and a ruddy complexion approached from the other direction, his body slithering from side to side as he plodded over the slippery ground. It was Chi Chung-hsiang, on his way to Lien-niu's house to consult her about going to the cotton fields the next day to deal with the insects. The truth was that these days he was glad to have any excuse to call on her. As the two came face to face, Chung-hsiang, seeing no one was around, whispered, "It's too muddy. Let me go and draw water for you. You'll only fall if you try to carry the buckets."

Lien-niu was obstinate. She got quite angry when anyone suggested that something was beyond her powers. "Out of my way!" she said—half smiling, half angry. "We'll see if I fall." Chung-hsiang hesitated, then let her slip past and go on her way. As she passed him she said in a low voice, "There's a pair of shoes at home. See if they fit you." Then she took to her heels. Chung-hsiang stood there undecided for a moment, then followed her. Lien-niu had just filled her second bucket when he arrived. He picked up the pole, slung a bucket at either end, and started back.

When he had emptied the water into the jar, Lien-niu pulled up a chair and asked him to rest. Smiling, she called to her mother, "Mother, shall we give that pair of shoes to Chung-hsiang now?"

"Why not?" her mother replied.

"It's very kind of you, Mother Yuan," said Chung-hsiang shyly, "but I . . ."

Mother Yuan glanced at him tenderly. "Now then, not another word! You're a member of our team, and that's like being one of the family. You've helped us time and again in the fields and round the house. It's a fair exchange—work for work—so take the shoes and wear them."

Chung-hsiang tried them on, and Lien-niu was delighted at the perfect fit. Then the three of them began to talk about other things.

Toward the end of the conversation, Chung-hsiang mentioned that the rain had caused insects to appear on the fruit trees again.

"Many?" Lien-niu asked in alarm.

"Quite a few," Chung-hsiang answered.

"Then let's mix up some insecticide today. The ground should be dry enough to spray tomorrow."

They talked for a while longer, then Chung-hsiang took his shoes—made just the way he liked them—and left.

A south wind rose in the night, and the next day there was not a cloud in the sky. By the afternoon, the sandy ground was firm underfoot again.

Chung-hsiang and Lien-niu were ladling insecticide into buckets when Li Feng-lan, a member of their team, called from outside.

"Chung-hsiang! Lien-niu! Everybody's here. Hurry up and bring your things."

"Com-ing! Com-ing!" Lien-niu shouted cheerfully.

She slung the sprayer over her shoulder while Chung-hsiang lifted the buckets of insecticide on a pole.

As they stepped out of the house, they saw a man coming toward them, muttering to himself. This was Whiskers Li, Lien-niu's maternal uncle. He was about fifty years old, and a few solitary whiskers hung forlornly from his lip. He had once been a small-time cattle dealer, but was a laboring man as well. During the land reform he was classified as a well-to-do peasant.

A grandmother making slippers

Chung-hsiang sensed something was amiss and came to a stop with the buckets still on his shoulder. But he heard Lien-niu's voice behind him, calling out affectionately to Whiskers Li, "Hello, Uncle. Mother's inside. I'm sorry I can't make you tea, but the team is waiting for us in the village square. You go on in." Then she called inside to alert her mother, "Mother, Uncle has come. Give him a nice beaten-up egg, with sugar and hot water!" Then, half walking and half skipping, she hurried to the village square.

Lien-niu's father had died when she was twelve, leaving her and her mother with not a square inch of land, nor even a roof over their heads. Finding themselves entirely without support, they had gone to live with Whiskers Li and stayed several years. During that time, Mother Yuan did household chores and worked in the fields, so that she was almost as good as an extra hand. Lien-niu, though only a girl, would take the cattle to graze, mow grass, gather firewood—in short, do half the job of a grown-up. On the whole, then, Whiskers Li had nothing to complain of; for they were his close relations and they worked hard. Yet he would constantly brag about how much he had done for them. His wife, for her part, never lost a chance to show Mother Yuan up to bad advantage, either to her face or behind her back. She often made references to "people who live on others and do nothing," or some such nasty remark. Naturally, Mother Yuan found life in her brother's house unbearable.

After Liberation, she took her daughter and returned to her own village. On the land she was allotted during the land reform, she set up a household of her own. Lien-niu was fifteen by then, and, at the behest of Whiskers Li, was engaged to her cousin, the son of her mother's youngest sister.

Life had gone smoothly in the new society, and in three years Lien-niu had become a grown-up girl of eighteen. Raised in the hard school of poverty and struggle, she was a capable worker with plenty of spirit. She caught on to new ideas quickly and was one of the most active members of the village and the Youth League.

Last winter, the villagers made use of the slack season to repair a dike. On the final day of the job, Lien-niu, Feng-lan, and a few other girls were leaning against the dyke, snatching a bit of rest—for the weather was warm. They were amusing themselves throwing pebbles into the water, when Chung-hsiang, who was passing by, noticed a crack appear in part of the earthwork. Without hesitation, he rushed over and propped up the embankment with his back, shouting "Run!" at the top of his voice to the girls. They had hardly got clear when the earth collapsed. Chung-hsiang's back was badly hurt.

Since that time, Lien-niu had taken a special interest in him. She would sometimes quietly make him a pair of shoes or pour hot tea for him when they were working in the fields. For his part, Chung-hsiang began to sense a feeling of warmth whenever he was with Lien-niu. He noticed she was always the first to volunteer for any work, and this energy of hers seemed to give him strength. Undoubtedly, the same thing was on their minds, but neither cared to speak about it.

Everyone in the village guessed, of course—especially the younger people, who looked on it as their own affair and thought the two would make an excellent match.

Whiskers Li also noticed how his niece had joined the mutual-aid team, gone to meetings regularly, enrolled in political study classes, and had dealings with the district and county offices. He was also aware that the last two years had seen the advent of the Marriage Law—a subject that had been on the lips of the young people constantly. The matter of Chung-hsiang and Lien-niu disturbed him deeply. Supposing his niece should break her engagement to her cousin?

That is why he had dropped in at Mother Yuan's house. He believed that nothing could be better than to have an aunt for one's mother-in-law. This double family relationship would, he thought, be to Lien-niu's advantage. Besides, this was a match of his own initiation, and if Lien-niu did not marry the man of his choice, where would his prestige be? Furthermore, he had looked after her since she was a child. He had been father and uncle to her. She ought to listen to him, for he had every right to see her well settled. "The widow and the orphan," he would often say to himself, "do not know the world." He felt duty-bound to handle his niece's marriage.

He knew that the Marriage Law had been promulgated for over a year, but he had his own ideas about it. This law, he thought, must surely ruin the "general state of human affairs." Since the time of his forefathers, had there ever been a marriage without a matchmaker? Nowadays, when he saw boys and girls together, he would shake his head and say, "Everything about the Communists is good except this Marriage Law, which fairly turns my stomach."

Now, seating himself near the door, he took a few puffs on his pipe and said, "Lien-niu's aunt asked me to tell you that she would like the wedding to take place soon."

Mother Yuan hesitated. "Why, the child is hardly grown up," she said. "Surely we can wait a few years before we discuss such a question."

Whiskers Li noted the clouded expression on her face, the restraint in her voice. "Could it be that the wind has already changed?" he thought to himself, taking a few more puffs. Then he spoke aloud in a persuasive tone. "The sooner the marriage is over the better. Then we will both be able to set our hearts at ease. The girl is running wild. If this goes on for long, who knows what might happen? I won't be the only one who is disgraced. Isn't that true?"

Not long before this, Mother Yuan had talked the matter over with Lien-niu. "I went to your father's house as a child-bride," she had said. "I was browbeaten and ill-treated and hardly a day went by when I wasn't in tears. Now the government has given us this Marriage Law. It's a very good law. You're eighteen, and you're not stupid. Your life's your own. But . . ." Mother Yuan's tone of voice changed. Lien-niu listened with lowered head, playing with the end of her plaits, feeling her face redden.

"But I was thinking," her mother went on, "that if you married into your aunt's family, I'd have someone to look after me when I'm old . . ." Her voice trailed off again.

Lien-niu, seeing her mother was still worried about her old age, said gently, "Mother, I've thought this over often. You know the old saying, 'Better to depend on yourself than on relatives and neighbors.' Someone else's rice may taste all right, but it's hard to digest. You know what that aunt of mine is like. She turns nasty over the merest trifle. She's impossible to live with." Tears appeared in Mother Yuan's eyes as she listened.

"Things are different these days," Lien-niu went on. "We don't have to rely on charity. We're in a mutual-aid team; we can both work; we can support ourselves. Chung-hsiang was saying we'd soon have producers' cooperatives, with nurseries for working mothers. So there'll still be a job for you, even when you find the going too hard in the fields."

The mother's head was nodding in agreement as her daughter spoke, for these words struck a sympathetic chord in her heart. "Anyway," Lien-niu continued, "without boasting, I'm sure I'll be able to support you for the rest of your life. These days a daughter is as good as a son. I can earn as many work-points as Chung-hsiang or any other member of the team. And later we'll be living in a socialist society. It's a broader and broader road we're traveling, Mother." Her mother smiled.

Lien-niu's words betrayed her heart. Recently, in their talks on family matters, it was always Chung-hsiang this and Chung-hsiang that. By now the mother knew pretty well what was on the girl's mind.

This made it doubly awkward when Whiskers Li brought up the subject, for Mother Yuan knew she was torn between two strong pulls. "On one side," she thought, "I have my daughter, my own flesh and blood. On the other, I have my sister to think of and my own brother who is the matchmaker. I can't tell them how Chung-hsiang and Lien-niu feel about each other, because there is nothing definite about the relationship. And besides, to say to my brother's face that my daughter has fallen in love—why, I'd feel so ashamed that I wouldn't know where to start!"

Reasoning in this way within herself, Mother Yuan decided to put the matter off if she could. "Ah," she said to her brother, "when a girl grows up she has a mind of her own. The wing has feathered. Who can tell if she will listen to you?"

"Humph!" Whiskers Li retorted angrily, tugging at his tobacco pouch. "No matter how high the mountain is, it cannot hide the sun. A daughter can't act on her own if her mother is there to guide her."

"But, Brother," said Mother Yuan with some effort, "you mustn't judge things by those old standards. Don't you see . . . ?"

"See what?"

When his sister did not answer, Whiskers Li too fell silent.

The shadows of the trees lengthened. The little girls who tended the cows and the sheep at pasture were driving the animals downhill. Crows and sparrows were circling over the treetops, homing to their nests.

Finally, Whiskers Li tapped out his pipe and got up. "It's getting late," he said. "I must be off." Mother Yuan invited him to stay the night, but he refused. "It's only ten *li*. I can cover that in no time."

Before he left, he gave some last-minute instructions. He reminded Mother Yuan that her sister owned land, had a big house, and was well off, and that it would be difficult to find another family like this. He added that they were the closest of relations, and that nothing could alter this fact. He also warned Mother Yuan not to provoke her sister.

Mother Yuan, however, would give him no promise. All she would say was: "We'll talk about it again later."

The rays from the paraffin lamp lit up the room brightly. Mother Yuan sat by a chest of drawers at the window, making shoes. As she worked, she turned the whole thing over in her mind. "If Lien-niu should break her engagement," she argued to herself, "how would we two sisters ever be able to face each other again? There would be a real family scandal. . . ." Then she remembered what her daughter had said. It sounded so true to her. But again the thought arose: "If my daughter should choose her own mate, there's bound to be gossip." Thus she went on pondering, her mind in a tangle. Just then the sound of the door latch roused her from her reverie.

Lien-niu entered. She blew out her lantern and hung it on the wall. Then she sat on the big chair in front of the table. Ordinarily, when she came back from the village school, she would read and write for some time, often until her mother had urged her two or three times to go to bed. But tonight she put her elbows on the table, rested her chin on her hands, and gazed at her mother.

"What did Uncle have to say?" she asked.

The mother assumed an air of innocence and said, "Why can't he just call on his sister to see how she is?"

"It must have been something that brought him here," Lien-niu insisted.

"Well, what do you think it was?"

Lien-niu became impatient. "Snow won't cover a corpse indefinitely!" she snapped.

"If you know already," said her mother with a forced smile, "why ask me?"

Lien-niu began to act like a child. Without warning, she snatched the shoe from her mother's hand and flung it at the wall. "Mother, tell me!" she cried, stamping her feet and making her chair creak in protest.

Mother Yuan's eyes shone with kindness. How could she let this high-spirited girl be married into a family not to her liking, and watch her spend the rest of her life in sorrow? Lovingly, she straightened the girl's hair and comforted her.

"There now," she said, "I'll tell you. I'll tell you."

Slowly and quietly, she began to recount every word that the uncle had said. As Lien-niu listened, anger filled her heart. When she heard that her aunt wanted the wedding to be soon, she thought she would choke, so big was the lump in her throat.

"What did you tell him?" she demanded.

The mother sighed deeply. "I didn't give him any definite answer," she replied.

Lien-niu stood up and pushed her chair back. "Mother, I don't like half-measures. We might as well make a clean break now. Let's go to the district government and apply for the annulment of my engagement."

The croaking of frogs in the paddy fields made her hesitate. She sat down and fidgeted nervously. Then a gust of south wind wafted in through the open window. It was cool and refreshing on her face. Her mind became clearer.

"Today we have the backing of the People's Government. Even one's parents must listen to reason, to say nothing of one's aunts and uncles. Feudal practices carry no weight today!"

Having expressed her point of view, she felt better. But she heard her mother give another deep sigh, and realized that she might have hurt her feelings. In a calmer tone, she began to explain.

"I'm not trying to brush my uncle aside," she said, pulling her chair up close to her mother. "I know how he must feel. But you know that cousin of mine as well as I do. He's so *dreary*. We played together when we were kids. But I never liked him. You know that."

Mother Yuan nodded.

"People will talk if we break the engagement," Lien-niu went on, "but you needn't worry. Who are they, anyway? Only a few old-fashioned gossips. If we act according to the Marriage Law, we'll be doing right."

Here the girl lowered her voice. "Mother, I never hide anything from you. You know . . ." Shyness overcame her, and her voice trailed off. But realizing she had to get it over with, she screwed up her courage and went on. "I've known Chung-hsiang for some time. I don't know whether it's his ideas, or the way he works, or his general attitude. . . .

Maybe it's his nature, his temperament, his ability, his looks. . . . Whatever it is . . ." It took all the gumption she had to get the next two words out. "I'm satisfied."

In her heart, Mother Yuan was so happy for her daughter that her worries vanished. She wanted to say she had known of this for a long time, but she was afraid of embarrassing Lien-niu. She simply said, "I like him, too. Everyone has a good word for him."

Lien-niu could not resist talking about Chung-hsiang. "When you're with a person of that caliber, it means you can help each other. Look at the way he works with people, look at his enthusiasm, see how dependable he is. His team members are all for him. When they become a co-op, he's sure to be elected chairman. . . ."

It was late, but the mother and daughter were so absorbed that they talked on into the small hours. Finally, the sound of their voices woke the rooster, who, thinking his mistresses had risen, bestirred himself, flapped his wings, and began to crow.

The next day, after supper, an urgent notice came from the township government. All carts from the villages were needed to transport grain from the district depots to the railway station. The job was to start that very night.

Three carts from Chung-hsiang's team would be going. To draw one of them, Chung-hsiang harnessed the ox from his own family and the one from Lien-niu's household together.

As Lien-niu was getting the bundles of straw ready, along with the feed and the odds and ends needed for the trip, Li Feng-lan, whip in hand, came in and asked hurriedly, "Lien-niu, does your mother mind you going out with the carts?" This stocky young wife had a special regard for the girl's welfare.

"No, she doesn't mind," Lien-niu answered, smiling.

"That's all right, then," Li Feng-lan continued. "I was

afraid she might. . . ." Mother Yuan's voice came from inside the house. "Who's that? Is that Feng-lan?"

"Yes, Mother Yuan," the woman replied. "Is it all right for Lien-niu to go with the carts tonight? There'll be quite a few girls and young daughters-in-law going."

"Of course it's all right," said Mother Yuan. "This is a very worthwhile job." After a pause, she added, "She's very young. You will keep an eye on her, won't you?"

The string of ox carts set out soon after nightfall. Wheels rumbled; tobacco pipes glowed; voices floated through the air. Despite the darkness, no one felt lonely.

When they first left the village, Chung-hsiang walked beside the cart, holding the reins, while Lien-niu followed behind to see that nothing fell off. After a while, Chung-hsiang stopped and said, "You don't have to worry. Nothing can possibly fall. Come, sit up in the cart."

"I don't mind going slowly like this," Lien-niu replied quietly.

Ignoring her answer, Chung-hsiang pulled on the reins. "Quick, get up," he called out. So Lien-niu climbed up and sat with her back against the bundles of straw. Chung-hsiang sat cross-legged beside her.

The cart bumped and rumbled on its way. In tune with the ceaseless sound of the wheels, an unending train of thought unfolded in the minds of these two young people.

They had worked together, studied together, and loved each other for a long time. People remarked that they were like one person, as close as the ear and the cheek or the man and his shadow. They looked up to each other, and they tried to outdo each other. They talked and joked a great deal when they were together, yet neither had ever broached the subject of their relationship. They had both wanted to, but had somehow never found the right moment.

It was dark and still. The carts in front had drawn far ahead; those behind were a long way back. This was a good time for a heart-to-heart talk. But neither of them seemed able to speak.

In the end, Chung-hsiang broke the silence. "Are you awake?" he asked. His voice had a choking sound in it, and he cleared his throat immediately after he had spoken.

Lien-niu was certainly not sleeping. From the moment she had started preparing for this journey, she had felt absurdly happy. Now, on the cart, her thoughts had been running on and on, far into the future. She did not know when she first realized that someone loved her. Her mother, of course, thought her dearer than life itself. But this love was different. She wanted to tell Chung-hsiang of her conversation with her mother. It would make him happy. But how could a girl say such things to a boy? Then she began to think about the village and the future and how they would organize a co-operative. That looked very promising. If she could only live with Chung-hsiang forever. . . .

In the fields beside the road, the grain shoots swayed in the breeze. High in the sky above, the glittering stars of the Milky Way seemed to be winking at her. A feeling of sweetness swept over her.

It was as she was indulging in these pleasant reveries that Chung-hsiang's voice came to her ears, asking if she was asleep. She was startled, and blushed. Then, feigning composure, she rubbed her eyes and said, "No, I'm not asleep."

Chung-hsiang touched the bullocks gently with his whip and shouted at them. Then he racked his brains for the next thing to say. Finally, he came up with a question: "What did your mother say about us going out together tonight?"

"She didn't mind," said Lien-niu mildly. "Even if she did, it wouldn't matter."

Again Chung-hsiang shouted at the animals. Then, after another long pause, he blurted out, "We two . . ." The rest of the sentence was never uttered. His heart pounded, his ears sang, his lips grew dry, and his voice faded away.

Sensing the seriousness of the approaching conversation, Lien-niu felt herself becoming tense. She managed to pull herself together, just as Chung-hsiang tried another approach.

"I feel I have so much to tell you," he began.

It was as though they were parted by a thin sheet of window paper, but it was as difficult to tear as iron.

Chung-hsiang reasoned to himself: "There are only the two of us here. If I say the wrong thing, it can't matter too much." He made a final effort: "Lien-niu, I want to talk to you about us." His voice was shaky, but he felt better when he had spoken. Turning, he waited for Lien-niu's reply.

But she said nothing.

She was thinking of her engagement, and of her uncle, that pig-headed man with a mind full of feudal ideas. She was thinking of her aunt, who was a difficult woman. It was no use hoping to solve the problem through reason. Yet if they made a clean break, her mother would lose both her brother and her sister, her only close relatives. She remembered her uncle's visit two days before. Neither he nor his sister would ever forget or forgive if the engagement were broken. Of course, they would have to accept it sooner or later. But it would not be a pleasant business.

She was brooding on these thoughts when Chung-hsiang spoke to her, and it was this that made her hesitate for a long moment, and finally say with a sigh, "It's not so easy."

Chung-hsiang had sat there waiting for her to answer. Instead, there was what seemed an endless silence, and then some remark about it not being easy. In desperation, he jumped down off the cart.

Lien-niu turned, and was startled to see him walking. "What did you get down for?" she asked.

Chung-hsiang muttered: "It feels better this way."

It was not hard to see he was displeased. So Lien-niu smiled and said, "Come on up. I'm not a tiger. I won't eat you." Somewhat reassured, Chung-hsiang got up again. Lien-

niu at once took hold of his large hands, whip and all, and
held them tightly in hers.

The cart rumbled on. The oxen were tired and plodded
slowly along. They needed no guidance on the well-beaten
track, so that Chung-hsiang and Lien-niu could sit in silence,
holding each other's hands.

Chung-hsiang was about to say something when he heard
a cart approaching from behind, and a voice urging and
cursing the animals. Withdrawing his hands from Lien-niu's
grasp, he jumped to the ground. The second cart slowed
as it approached and the voice called "Who is that ahead?"
"We're from Yuan Village," Chung-hsiang shouted back,
"where are you from?" "Is that you, Chung-hsiang?" said
the voice in the darkness.

Now Lien-niu recognized the voice. The man was none
other than her uncle, Whiskers Li. "Good Heavens! I would
meet *him* the night I go out with the carts!" They were
seized by a kind of panic. "Whip the animals up!" Lien-niu
urged in a whisper.

Chung-hsiang lashed at the oxen and they soon left
Whiskers Li behind. But before long they found their way
blocked by the carts in front, so he caught up with them.
His first question made Chung-hsiang bristle with resent-
ment: "Whose beast is that you have harnessed in your
cart?"

Lien-niu, hiding on top of the load, braced herself for
Chung-hsiang's answer.

Chuang-hsiang did not want trouble, but Whiskers Li had
him in a corner. He decided not to beat about the bush. "Oh,
one of them belongs to Lien-niu's family," he answered, as
casually as he could.

Whiskers Li was in no mood to trifle. "She hasn't come
tonight, has she?" he asked immediately.

"Yes, she's here."

Whiskers Li exploded: "What! Lien-niu here?" he bellowed. "This is utter nonsense! Where is she? Where is she?" He was trembling all over with uncontrolled rage.

At this point, Lien-niu decided there was little use in hiding. "I'm here, Uncle," she said calmly, sitting up.

When Whiskers Li heard Lien-niu's voice, he behaved as if the sky were falling on him. "What are you doing here?" he roared. "Get yourself home this instant!"

"Uncle, there's no need to fly into a rage," said Lien-niu, holding her ground.

"Get down from there, I say! Get down!"

"Uncle, many of the womenfolk have come out tonight. It's quite all—"

"If you don't come down, I'll drag you down!"

All this time, the carts had continued on their way. Now Whiskers Li ordered Chung-hsiang to stop. Chung-hsiang, who was seething with anger, ignored him. Then, remembering that the man was Lien-niu's maternal uncle, he tried to suppress his indignation. "Uncle Li," he said, "there's no need to make a fuss."

Whiskers Li made a gesture of fury with his whip, but Lien-niu quickly jumped down from the cart and faced him. "Uncle, it's my job to go out when there's grain to be carted. I came of my own free will. What right have you to interfere in what doesn't concern you? Why are you trying to pick a quarrel? I've done nothing wrong. As the saying goes: 'If their hearts are pure, nuns and monks can sit together.'"

"You are a shameless hussy!" Whiskers Li yelled. "Get home! Get home!"

"I'm not going home. You can't tell me what do do!"

"Oh, can't I, though? An uncle is like a father. You have no father, so you're under my care."

Lien-niu did not give an inch. "It's because you're my uncle that I make allowances for you. You should appreciate that."

"How dare you talk back to me like that!" Whiskers Li snatched up his whip by the stock and made to thrash Lien-niu with it. But his arm was immediately grasped from behind.

The other carts had long since come to a stop, and the men and women in them were watching the scene. Opinions differed: Some sided with the uncle; some with the niece. "Women work the same as men these days. Why shouldn't they come with the carts? You'll never keep them under lock and key. The heavy hand's no good with girls nowadays." Others were saying: "Who knows what a girl could be up to, eh? These two might be getting a bit too friendly. Can't allow such goings-on. If she were my daughter, I wouldn't let her out." It was noticeable that those who took the young people's side spoke out clearly, while those who sympathized with Whiskers Li only whispered.

Li Feng-lan pushed her way through the crowd and confronted Whiskers Li. "Uncle Li," she said persuasively, "you can see how many women and girls there are here. Lien-niu's not the only one."

Whiskers Li stood with his arms akimbo, panting. "Feng-lan," he said, "she says it's not my job to tell her what to do! But you know that it *is* my job!"

"It's your job," Feng-lan replied, "only if you tell her to do the right thing."

Whiskers Li began to splutter, but Feng-lan was worried that this argument would upset their schedule. "If there's anything else to say, let's say it at home," she suggested. "We can't have private affairs interfering with the job like this. We have to get this grain onto the train. Come on." She turned to the crowd. "Break it up. We've got to be moving, and quickly!"

The front carts moved off, but Whiskers Li stood where he was. Li Feng-lan pushed Lien-niu back toward her cart. "Come on, I'll sit with you two. Up we go!"

Lien-niu was upset. After all, she was only a young girl. Overcome with embarrassment and exasperation, she began to cry. Li Feng-lan put her arm around her and comforted her. "Don't cry. When you get home, you can settle it peacefully. There's nothing that can't be straightened out." Then, turning to Chung-hsiang, she told him to hurry and catch up with the others.

Chung-hsiang glared at Whiskers Li, then brought his whip down hard on the oxen.

"Why take it out on dumb animals?" asked Li Feng-lan.

Whiskers Li drove behind them for a while, hooting and spitting at them. But the knowledge that Li Feng-lan was with them eventually calmed him, and he let his cart drop back.

Feng-lan and Lien-niu, leaning back arm-in-arm against the straw, talked quietly together.

"It's not easy for old people to get used to new ways," said Feng-lan.

"But why on earth should he make such a fuss?" Lien-niu wiped her eyes and straightened her hair. "When he gets back, he'll start the whole thing again."

She had told Feng-lan about Chung-hsiang long before, so there were no secrets between them. Feng-lan tried to comfort her by saying, "An old die-hard like your uncle won't come round at the first try. But you needn't be scared of him, because you have the Marriage Law on your side. Have you discussed it with your mother?"

"Mother's not against it. I think the sooner we register, the better."

"Let's not take any short cuts. We should settle things with your aunt first. Anyway, when we get back from this trip, we'll go to the district office and apply for the annulment of your engagement."

"They won't take it lying down."

"But you'll have the government behind you."

The sunflowers were tilting their heads toward the sun;

strings of beans hanging from the rack were swaying in the breeze. Red peppers, half hidden behind green leaves, looked like cornelians. The vegetable plot was not big, but it had almost every vegetable in season.

It was nearly noon and Mother Yuan, a blue kerchief over her head, was busy digging. The sound of cart wheels reached her ears, and she looked up and saw that it was Chung-hsiang coming. A daughter is never far from a mother's thoughts, and when Mother Yuan saw no sign of Lien-niu on the cart she began to worry.

As Chung-hsiang pulled up and saw the question in her eyes, he blushed. "She's gone with Li Feng-lan to the district government."

Mother Yuan suddenly saw this young man not as the neighbor's boy, Chi Chung-hsiang, but as one of her own family. She could not help staring at her future son-in-law—to his acute embarrassment—and what she saw she liked, to the smallest detail.

When Chung-hsiang had watered the animals, he went to the township government, where he received an assurance that if he and Lien-niu wanted to marry, no one could stop them.

Around noon the next day, Lien-niu was still not back. Mother Yuan was so agitated that she kept going out to look. The two days her daughter had been gone seemed like an age. She wanted to cook something nice for her and had thought of killing a chicken; but the hens were all laying eggs, and she did not feel like losing one of them. Besides, she could never summon up the courage to kill a fowl. So she went to get some eggs. She had reached the threshold of the inner room when a shadow fell across the wall. Turning, she saw her brother, Whiskers Li. His face was puffy, and he sat down by the wall without a word. Mother Yuan felt a chill down her spine but greeted him cordially. His grudging acknowledgment meant that a storm was brewing.

All her life, this old woman had been timid and afraid to get involved in anything. Her cheerfulness gave way to nervousness when she recalled that Lien-niu had gone to the district government.

"What sort of discipline do we have in this family?" Whiskers Li demanded angrily. "She didn't tell you anything about it, eh?" His eyes flashed as he emptied his pipe on the ground. "So you've thrown your regard for the old generation to the winds?"

Mother Yuan tried to control her anxiety. "If you have anything to say, Brother, please say it quietly."

"Why did you send her out with the carts?"

"We have no man in the family—"

"Then there's no need for anyone to go!"

"But quite a few girls went from our village."

Whiskers Li said nothing, just looked at his sister as though she were a child who had to be taught things. Finally, he said, "If I hadn't looked on you as my own family, would I have taken you and your daughter in? I can't remember how many times I quarreled with my wife over you two. You know this. You know I took care of you once, and I'm trying my best to take care of you now. Why would I do all this, if it weren't for your own good? When Lien-niu goes to her aunt's house, she'll be treated with special consideration. And when you get old, your nephew will take you in. Isn't that clear?"

Seeing that Mother Yuan did not talk back, he supposed she was beginning to see reason. "On the other hand," he went on, "consider the family background of that good-for-nothing Chi Chung-hsiang. In the old days, he was a cowherd. He hadn't a brick or a beam to his name. He got a little land a couple of years ago, of course, but he's got no roots in the village. If your daughter marries him, what will she get out of it? Now, our sister's family has always owned land. You'll never be short of anything there. You'd better send the girl as quickly as you can to her aunt's home."

Mother Yuan no longer knew what to think. With a deep sigh, she said, "You've got to let us talk it over between ourselves."

"Talk what over? What the mother says goes, that's all there is to it!"

"You don't know my daughter."

"Well, if you can't control her, you ought to be ashamed to live! Look, you consented to this match when it was made. You can no more go back on your word now than scrape your spittle off the ground!"

Mother Yuan suddenly realized that she was sick of this bickering. "Brother," she said, flushing red in the face, "she's a grown-up girl. When it comes to marriage, not even the government can decide the matter for her—much less I."

"That mongrel Chi!" Whiskers Li shouted. "So he's used the Marriage Law as an excuse to seduce women, has he? Flogging to death would be too good for him!"

Mother Yuan took the bull by the horns. None too gently, she said, "It's no good, brother. They're both willing."

Whiskers Li's rage boiled over. At the sight of this meek sister of his arguing the point with him, he was so exasperated that he kicked a small table over, upsetting a needle basket that was on top of it. Gesticulating wildly, he roared, "Let me tell you, if you think you can break the engagement, you're dreaming! You'll lose face, I warn you. Perhaps you've forgotten that the district head is related by marriage to your sister. . . ."

They argued until sunset, getting no closer to agreement. Then Lien-niu, in high-spirits, rushed into the courtyard. She was hot and flushed. "Have you missed me, Mother?" she called. "Come and see the fine cloth I've bought!"

She stopped short on the threshold. Her mother was sitting on a bundle of straw, her chin on her hands and her eyes full of tears. The small table lay upside down on the floor. Sitting by the wall, glaring straight ahead as he filled his pipe, was her uncle.

She was furious. She flung the roll of cloth down with a bang, whipped off her straw hat, and stood there fanning her face very rapidly.

The tears trickled down Mother Yuan's face. Lien-niu turned to her. "Why are you crying?" she asked. "I'm responsible for my own affairs!"

Whiskers Li fixed her with bloodshot eyes. "You can't break your engagement!" he snapped.

Lien-niu raised her eyebrows. "I'm the one who'll decide that!"

"It's not for you to decide," said Whiskers Li, pointing a finger at her.

"It's still less for *you* to decide!"

"I'm your uncle!"

"You can arrange your own daughter's marriage, but not mine!"

Whiskers Li tried to assert his authority. "You're coming with me today!" he said harshly.

It was Lien-niu's turn to point. "I am a citizen of this country. I have my liberty. I am *not* going anywhere with you. Touch me if you dare!"

Mother Yuan had stopped weeping and was now gazing in amazement at her daughter. How the girl had grown! The sight gave her strength.

By this time, a crowd had started to gather. Some were talking in the courtyard; others had come inside to reconcile the quarrelers. Once again, opinions were divided as to who was in the right.

A woman with a baby in her arms saw that the argument was serious and told the girl next to her to hurry off and fetch the district head.

"Where shall I find her?" the girl asked.

"At Li Feng-lan's. She arrived a while ago on her bicycle."

The district head had that very morning met Lien-niu's cousin at the fair. She had taken him into her office and told him exactly why Lien-niu wanted to break the engagement.

At the same time, she had patiently explained the Marriage Law to him. Finally, she had said: "Brother, if Lien-niu doesn't want to marry you and you force her into it, you won't have a moment's peace. Now when you go home, you try to persuade your mother not to be angry with Lien-niu. Any marriage contracted by a third party is against the Marriage Law."

Perhaps young people are less pig-headed than their elders, for, when the boy had heard the district head's argument to the end, he gave in with a good grace.

The district head had intended to visit Yuan Village that day anyway, so after lunch she jumped on her bicycle and pedaled off.

She was a tall woman of about thirty, who dressed in a blue uniform and wore her hair bobbed. She was kind, but there was a strong vein of seriousness underneath. Now, as she came with Li Feng-lan into Mother Yuan's courtyard— closely followed by a very embarrassed Chung-hsiang—she took in the situation at a glance. To the women gathered in the courtyard, she offered a simple greeting, and then strode into the house.

Li Feng-lan followed, leaving Chung-hsiang surrounded by the crowd. He was ill at ease, but he was ready to fight it out with Whiskers Li. His eyes were wide, his breathing was jerky; when people smiled at him he did not respond.

When the district head entered the room, Mother Yuan, wiping away tears, pulled up a bench for her. The district head took Lien-niu by the hand and sat down with her, smiling.

Whiskers Li was at first in high spirits; for this young woman was the wife of his sister's nephew. But when he saw how friendly she was with Lien-niu and when he noticed that Chung-hsiang—that brazen fellow—had come too, he began to have misgivings. He comforted himself with the thought that the smile on the district head's face was no indication of her feelings; in the new society, government

Mechanical rice-transplanters in
the fields of Kwantung province

officials usually went about their work with a smile. Still, he
was uneasy. He eyed the woman carefully and said, "May I
ask whether you've talked to Lien-niu's aunt?"

"Yes, some time ago," the district head replied, caressing
Lien-niu's hand.

"And has everything been explained?" Whiskers Li asked,
his eyes narrowing.

"Everything," said the woman simply.

Mother Yuan looked from her to Whiskers Li, and her
heart began to thump. But Whiskers Li was overjoyed. An
expression of satisfaction spread over his face. "Tell me," he
said, "as a maternal uncle, haven't I the right to look after
my niece's interests?"

"Of course. A maternal uncle is a very close relation. What
is more, you have looked after Lien-niu since she was a child.
You're almost a father to her."

Whiskers Li looked highly gratified. "Now that is what I
call justice!" he exclaimed. Turning to the mother and daughter, he said, "No wonder she's a district head. She knows
what justice is." Then he turned back and asked, "So you
think I'm working in Lien-niu's best interests?"

"Of course," said the district head. "Everyone wants to
help a girl get a good husband."

"That's right!" said Whiskers Li, happy beyond words. "That's absolutely right! You are an honest official. You've said all there is to say." And he flashed Lien-niu and her mother a scornful look, as if to say, "We'll see whether I have authority over you or not!"

He had never felt better in his life. He was convinced that the district head had come to persuade Lien-niu to go to her aunt's house. Pointing at the girl, he remarked confidently to the district head, "She's very stubborn, you know. She refused to go!"

"Oh?" said the woman, still smiling. "Why would that be? Why would she be so stubborn about it?"

"Ask her yourself," said Whiskers Li.

The district head glanced at Lien-niu, then turned back to Whiskers Li. "I'd like *you* to tell me," she said.

Whiskers Li replied: "She said I took matters into my own hands, that I arranged the match."

"And did you? Was the match made without her approval?"

Whiskers Li was going to say that the engagement was arranged personally by the two families, which were very close, and that it was a good match, whichever way you looked at it. But somehow the words did not come out smoothly.

The district head's face took on a serious expression. When Whiskers Li had finished, she spoke slowly and clearly. "It is good that you meant well. But older people do not always see eye to eye with their sons and daughters. . . ."

Some of the exuberance faded from Whiskers Li. Mother Yuan, on the other hand, felt the lump in her throat begin to disappear.

"Some elderly folk cling to outmoded ideas," the district head went on. "They make arbitrary decisions about the marriage of their children. This is not right. They should know that the People's Government has given us the Marriage Law precisely to put an end to this practice, so that sons and daughters can choose their own marriage partners."

Her words were simple, but their effect on the listeners was dramatic. The silence was such that you could have heard a pin drop. Then a white-haired woman spoke up: "Heavens, yes! Think of the women in our villages around here. How many thought of killing themselves in the past? This has changed."

The woman with the baby in her arms went on. "No one dares to look on women as domestic animals today. Take my husband. Before Liberation he used to say, 'The horse I bought with my money I can ride or whip as I like!' We had so many quarrels that we never got any work done. Sometimes the weeds were higher than the crops. And the worse things got, the more we argued. What a time that was! Now, things have changed. You'd hardly know my husband. He never talks that kind of nonsense, and he works happily from dawn to dusk."

The district head smiled. "The Marriage Law was drafted for a purpose," she said, looking straight at Whiskers Li. "Its aim is to promote harmony in the family, so that we can get on with our work and bring prosperity for millions and millions of families."

Lien-niu stood up then and addressed Whiskers Li. "If a person is in the right, he doesn't have to obey even his father. You are my maternal uncle. I am prepared to give in to you on many things; but when it comes to the question of my marriage, I will obey neither you nor my father, should he rise from the dead."

These words pierced Whiskers Li to the heart. He stood there, speechless. The district head walked across to him. "Old Uncle," she said, "I've spoken to Lien-niu's cousin about the matter. He's willing to break the engagement. So there's nothing more to be said, is there? Come on, cheer up! I'll get your niece to cook you some supper. It's well past sunset."

Whiskers Li shook his head and growled, "I'm not hungry."

Li Feng-lan came up, hand-in-hand with Lien-niu. Pointing out Chung-hsiang, she said, "What do you think, friends? Won't these two make a fine match?"

A gust of laughter went up from the crowd. The woman with the baby shouted, "We said ages ago that if those two didn't become a pair, there'd be drought for three years, for Heaven itself couldn't bear to see them apart." This remark met with a murmur of approval.

Whiskers Li had a sneaking suspicion that these people were probably right. But they seemed to be making fun of him and in front of that young pup Chung-hsiang, too. He was indignant. Besides, from time immemorial, it had been the right of the parents to arrange their children's marriages. It was ridiculous to have this age-old custom wiped away so quickly and so easily. He was tempted to go on arguing, but he saw he had no chance against such a big crowd. No one there would back him up. It was useless.

He got up stiffly, and walked out. Someone tried to pull him back but failed. He turned his head as he left and said, "I shall have nothing more to do with this branch of my family." With this, he strutted off.

"Brother . . ."

Mother Yuan stood with her hand on the latch and called after him. But he was already disappearing into the distance.

The district head was about to take her leave. Turning to Lien-niu and Chung-hsiang, she asked, "Well? When are you two coming to register?"

They smiled but did not answer.

PART TWO

Building a New China

Mao Tse-tung

SERVE THE PEOPLE

[Part I has given us some idea of what China has been through in the last hundred years. We have seen how internal and external factors combined to make life intolerable for large sections of the Chinese population, and how this gave rise to a protracted struggle for independence from foreign control and for liberation from the oppressive power of the ruling classes within Chinese society.

In Part II we shall look at a very different China—the China that has emerged since 1949. We shall find a people obsessed with the urge to build, rejuvenated by the establishment of peace after so much war, and eager to tackle the mammoth task of remaking a nation from scratch.

It is often said that revolutions destroy but are not good at building. Yet China's Revolution triggered off some of the most creative and productive years in Chinese history. This vast country, with a minimum of foreign aid, managed not only to provide food, clothing, housing, and employment for her people but also to make great progress in industrialization, science, education, health, and the development of a modern agriculture.

There are two reasons for China's success, and they are closely related. The first can be located in the people themselves: the quantity of sheer energy—both physical and spiritual—generated in them by the Revolution. Without this drive, no government, whether communist or not, could possibly have led China into the modern world.

The second is the leadership the people have received. It would be foolish to play down the role of the Communist Party; and equally foolish to exaggerate it. The Party, has never amounted to much more than 2 per cent of the population, so it cannot take all the credit for China's progress. That—and the Party is the first to agree —must go to the people. But the people—and they are quick to admit it—have been well led by the Communists, particularly during the crucial 1950's.

The strength of the Communists lay partly in what they did *not* do. Unlike the governments of so many newly independent countries, they did not allow the creative spirit of the Revolution to dissipate itself in competitiveness and self-seeking. They did not encourage a privileged economic class to grow at the expense of the masses of the people but stressed that the whole society should advance together.

We shall see in Part III that this idea of a classless development was not accepted without opposition. There were fierce arguments about it within the Communist Party itself, arguments that came to a head in the Cultural Revolution.

During the 1950's, however, this dispute was not apparent. The Communists managed to strike a balance between the two contradictory elements that any leadership faces: the principle of *serving the people* and the job of *ruling the country*.

This balancing feat would not have been possible without the political philosophy of Mao Tse-tung. Mao has always insisted that leaders must serve. He has said more than once that if the Communist Party should forget its role as servant of the people, it would thereby become a hindrance instead of a help to the progress of China.

This idea has best been expressed in his two-page article entitled "Serve the People." This, the second of the "Three Old Favorites," was written in 1944, when the war against Japan was at its height. Mao singles out a very ordinary Party member, a soldier who was accidentally killed while working for the Revolution. He praises the man, emphasizing the need for all Party members to cultivate a similar dedication to the people, to be willing to accept criticism from the people, and to be prepared to die, if necessary, for the people.

It would not be too much to say that "Serve the People" has become to Chinese Communism what the Sermon on the Mount was to early Christianity. In it, Mao raises service to the level of martyrdom. Serving the people, he implies, is a religious ideal. Human life and death make sense only when they are dedicated to the welfare of others.

It is this deceptively simple idea—by no means unfamiliar to Western man—that has provided much of the impetus for China's progress.]

Our Communist Party and the Eighth Route and New Fourth Armies led by our Party are battalions of the Revolution. These battalions of ours are wholly dedicated to the liberation of the people and work entirely in the people's interests. Comrade Chang Ssu-teh* was in the ranks of these battalions.

All men must die, but death can vary in its significance. The ancient Chinese writer Ssuma Ch'ien said, "Though death befalls all men alike, it may be heavier than Mount Tai or lighter than a feather."† To die for the people is heavier

---

* Comrade Chang Ssu-teh was a soldier in the Guards Regiment of the Central Committee of the Chinese Communist Party. A member of the Communist Party who loyally served the people's interests, he joined the Revolution in 1933, took part in the Long March, and was wounded in service. On September 5, 1944, when making charcoal in the mountains of Ansai County, northern Shensi Province, he was killed by the sudden collapse of a kiln.

† Ssuma Ch'ien, the famous Chinese historian of the 2d century B.C., was the author of the *Historical Records*.

than Mount Tai, but to work for the fascists and die for the exploiters and oppressors is lighter than a feather. Comrade Chang Ssu-teh died for the people, and his death is indeed heavier than Mount Tai.

If we have shortcomings, we are not afraid to have them pointed out and criticized, because we serve the people. Anyone, no matter who, may point out our shortcomings. If he is right, we will correct them. If what he proposes will benefit the people, we will act upon it. The idea of "better troops and simpler administration" was put forward by Mr. Li Ting-ming,* who is not a Communist. He made a good suggestion that is of benefit to the people, and we have adopted it. If, in the interests of the people, we persist in doing what is right and correct what is wrong, our ranks will surely thrive.

We hail from all corners of the country and have joined together for a common revolutionary objective. And we need the vast majority of the people with us on the road to this objective. Today we already lead base areas with a population of 91 million,† but this not enough; to liberate the whole nation, more are needed. In times of difficulty we must not lose sight of our achievements; we must see the bright future and pluck up our courage. The Chinese people are suffering; it is our duty to save them, and we must exert ourselves in struggle. Wherever there is struggle there is sacrifice, and death is a common occurrence. But we have the interests of the people and the sufferings of the great majority at heart, and when we die for the people it is a worthy death. Nevertheless we should do our best to avoid unnecessary sacrifices. Our cadres must show concern for every soldier, and all people in the revolutionary ranks must care for each other, must love and help one another.

* Li Ting-ming, an enlightened landlord of northern Shensi Province, was at one time elected Vice-Chairman of the Shensi-Kansu-Ninghsia Border Region Government.
† This was the total population of the Shensi-Kansu-Ninghsia Border Region and all other liberated areas in northern, central, and southern China.

From now on, when anyone in our ranks who has done some useful work dies, be he soldier or cook, we should have a funeral ceremony and a memorial meeting in his honor. This should become the rule. And it should be introduced among the people as well. When someone dies in a village, let a memorial meeting be held. In this way we express our mourning for the dead and we unite all the people.

THE MAKING OF

AN INNOVATOR

[China made up her mind in the nineteenth century that industry was the key to prosperity and power. She was defeated too often by industrialized Western nations for the message not to sink in.

Progress was slow before the Revolution. Foreign investment created a handful of industrial cities—islands of wealth in a vast sea of rural poverty. We know from our own history in the West that industrialization can be a painful process, involving the destruction of traditional life-styles and the alienation of people from each other. The Chinese suffered some of the pangs of this process without reaping any of the benefits, until the Communists swept out foreign capital and put industry at the service of the Chinese people.

When reconstruction began in 1949, China suffered from a lack of technicians and skilled workers and from the destruction of most of her heavy industry during the war years. To make matters worse, the United States blockaded her, making it hard for her to get raw materials. She was fortunate that the Soviet Union—then in a more friendly mood toward her Asian neighbor— agreed to help in establishing plants and training technical personnel.

The Chinese at first concentrated on rebuilding and expanding the urban industrial centers. New cities were constructed, and satellite towns sprang up around the old ones. Soviet influence was particularly noticeable in the emphasis on heavy rather than light industry and in the way the factories were organized.

The Great Leap Forward of 1958 was the first major attempt to break out of this pattern. A campaign to get factories and workshops established in the countryside was begun. The idea was not only to raise production dramatically but also to accustom the people to satisfying many of their own industrial needs.

We do not know how far this program succeeded. The Western press spoke mockingly of "backyard furnaces," and the general assumption was that the whole effort was a waste of money, time, and materials.

The Chinese have never admitted that the Great Leap Forward was a failure. On the contrary, they say, many of the new enterprises that started then have since flourished, while the experience gained by ordinary people in the art of industrial production and in the principle of self-reliance has proved invaluable.

The next extract was written by a Chinese worker. It is a somewhat stylized account of his life, describing his personal reaction to Liberation and to the various policies of the Party during the 1950's.

Some aspects of the story seem strange to us: Notice, in particular, the curious relationship of the worker to the authorities. He is not afraid to criticize them; he even writes a big poster accusing the technical department of cowardice and pastes it up on their door. And he in turn is criticized by them—not for the kind of mistake workers in the West might make but for shortcomings in his character! Imagine an American worker being called into the manager's office and warned against "conceit and complacency."

The account appeared in the April, 1960, issue of the magazine *China Reconstructs*. It is preceded by a brief editorial comment.]

Ma Hsueh-li, a young fitter at the Wuhan Heavy Machine

Tool Plant, has been elected a model worker or "pacemaker" several times in the past few years, chiefly for his pertinacity and ingenuity in devising more rapid and efficient ways of working. In 1959 alone, over sixty of his innovative proposals were adopted for general use.

In a country like China, where industry has grown with tremendous speed from poor and backward beginnings, the influence of the worker-innovator is mighty. Both by deed and example he can help advance the whole general level of industrial skill and productivity among the workers. This is why Ma Hsueh-li—and thousands like him—are singled out for distinction, and fostered and encouraged as models for others to follow.

Here is his own story, as told in a speech made to a provincial conference of labor heroes in 1959.

I was born in a small village in Shantung province. My father was a landless farm laborer and we were miserably poor. I was quite small when the war against Japan broke out and our area fell under cruel enemy occupation. The following year there was a plague of locusts where we lived, and things got so wretched that my father decided to pack up and take the whole family to Shenyang, where he had some relatives. He didn't know any work but farm-laboring, so they helped him set up a small cigarette stall. Later he became a tinker, found a place in a workshop, and occasionally made buckets and things to sell. But he didn't earn enough to support a family of five, and I had to go out and scavenge coal and other scraps in the streets.

When I was eleven I was put into a factory run by a Japanese firm. They called me an "apprentice" but what I mostly did was shift coke for more than ten hours a day. I never got enough to eat but I had more than my fill of beatings and curses. The life was so hard I ran away. Then I got into another Japanese-run factory where they said I could be trained as a turner. But because I'd only had one year at primary school, I couldn't calculate well enough to operate a lathe. At the end of three years I was still classed as an apprentice. I used to weep in those days at what I imagined was my fate.

In 1945, the Japanese surrendered. How happy we were! Now, we thought, everything would come right. My father agreed to let me attend school in the daytime so I could learn enough to become a skilled worker, and I helped him in the evenings. But things were still terrible under the Kuomintang * regime. Pretty soon father's business failed altogether and I had to leave school again. There wasn't enough to eat. We sold our patched clothes and bed covers, but all we could buy with the money was soya-bean cake—the residue left after crushing the beans, which farmers ordinarily use for fertilizer. Once my father, returning from the countryside with a small quantity of grain, was waylaid by Kuomintang soldiers, who took it and beat him up so terribly that he has never recovered his health.

It was not until after Liberation that I was able to go to school again. But this time my tuition was free and I even got a grant to pay for books and meals. By August, 1950, I managed to pass the entrance test for the Shenyang No. 1 Machine Tool Plant. I started as an apprentice, but because I already knew something about the job, I quickly got promoted to a regular worker. What a contrast then with the way it had been before! There were no more beatings, nobody could exploit us—we were really the masters of the plant! Comparing my new life with the old, I worked hard, feeling I would never be able to repay the debt I owed to the Communist Party and Chairman Mao.

The Korean War had already started by the time I entered the factory, and shortly afterwards the whole place started to

* Chiang Kai-shek's Nationalist Party

hum with the campaign to "Resist American Aggression and Aid Korea." Later, there was the campaign to suppress counter-revolutionaries. There were many meetings and discussions, during which I thought a lot about the bitter life we had had under the Japanese imperialists and the Kuomintang. This greatly raised my class consciousness, and I put even more effort into my work, thinking this was the way I could best contribute to the cause. But when the Communist Party called on us workers to use our initiative and find more efficient ways of increasing production and cutting down costs, I began to see that there was more to it than sheer physical effort.

I had already watched a demonstration by a Soviet expert of the high-speed cutting method used by skilled lathe operators in his country, but I had only marveled at his technique and wished I could master it. Now, however, the factory started to teach the workers the multiple-tool method (using more than one cutter at a time), and when I was put onto operating a Czechoslovak-built turret lathe, I got to work combining both methods and managed to increase the efficiency of over a dozen different jobs. This proved to me that you need to use your wits and learn the skills of other people as well as working hard yourself. I found I could often turn out far more than my quota. Because of this, I was given especially complex jobs to do, and the leadership paid a lot of attention to helping me sort out problems. The next thing I knew, I was elected top labor model of the whole plant.

From then on, I worked more energetically than ever. Under the guidance of the Communist Party, I started to study politics seriously. The General Line for the Period of Transition announced in 1953 showed what had to be done to carry out socialist industrialization and socialist transformation in agriculture, handicrafts, capitalist industry, and commerce. Then the first Five-Year Plan was published, and this showed the way ahead even more clearly. In October, 1954, I was accepted as a Party member. I felt so strong and enlightened that ideas for innovations came into my head all the time. By making adjustments on my lathe, I reduced the time for making a big gear from twenty hours to three and a half hours, and that was just one of these ideas. All of my achievements were not that wonderful, but the Party gave me a lot of encouragement and publicized my methods throughout the plant. That same year I was chosen as one of Shenyang's advanced workers.

But I'm afraid that all this distinction, and having my name in the newspapers, went to my head. I was invited to give talks in several factories and schools, and won first prize in a number of work contests. The trade union and the Youth League both asked me to serve on their committees and be-

Matchbox labels illustrating the accomplishments of the Great Leap Forward

fore long I had no less than six posts. Fancying myself a cut above the rest, I stopped listening to other people's opinions. I was head of my work team, and when anyone had trouble with a job, I wouldn't explain it to him but would make him stand down from his lathe and let me do it for him. This must have been humiliating for my mates, but I didn't think of their feelings.

It's quite true what Chairman Mao says: "Modesty helps one to progress; conceit makes one lag behind." Because I was so complacent I achieved very little, and at the beginning of 1955, when advanced workers were being nominated, my name was not put forward.

My Party group did its best to help me see my faults, and the Party branch secretary talked to me himself, very patiently. At first I felt indignant at this criticism. I told myself: "I don't *want* to be a model worker. It's too difficult to live up to. I'll just keep pace with the rest." But after some good hard talk from the Party and some painful thinking about the bitter life I'd led before the Liberation, I saw that this was no way for a Party member to behave and I'd better change my ways. Gradually I got my ideas sorted out and started to work hard to correct my shortcomings. My output went up, and in the autumn of 1955 I was elected an Active Young Builder of Socialism.

Shortly after this, I was transferred to a new machine-tool plant at Wuhan. As soon as I arrived, I was put in a Russian-language class with several others. We were all going to be sent to the Soviet Union for technical training! Imagine, a poor lad who seldom got enough to eat and could not go to school before Liberation—who could have dreamed that such a great experience could happen to me!

Learning another language was hard at first and I sometimes used to get up and study at three or four in the morning, until my teacher found out and reproved me for not getting proper sleep. After eleven months, when we could carry on normal conversation and knew the necessary technical terms in Russian, we set off on our exciting journey.

What a lot I learned in that short year in the Soviet Union! Comrade Ilya, my teacher in Leningrad, was a real model for a worker to follow. He let me tackle a very complex job on his lathe after I'd been with him only three days. "The time you spend here is very precious," he said. "You must learn as many difficult jobs as you can—you can study the easy ones in your own country."

The energetic and conscientious way in which the Soviet workers approached their jobs, their confident manner of tackling new things, and their true international spirit of comradely help for us Chinese workers left a very deep impression on me. I realized that the good life they have today did not come easily; if our country, still so poor, is to reach their level, we have to work hard as they did. My whole visit was a great education.

I got back to Wuhan in July, 1957. It made me really proud to have a part in this heavy machine-tool plant, the first of its kind in China, and I tried to use my new knowledge as best I could. When the Party's General Line for Socialist Construction was published in 1958, it was as if a floodlight had illumined my mind. The Party called on us to get rid of our old ideas about what was possible and what was impossible, and to use our initiative in a spirit of "dare to think, dare to speak, dare to act." I racked my brains to think what I could do, as a Communist, to help our country build socialism faster.

In February, 1958, I happened to be in a workshop where they were drilling 133-millimeter cylindrical tubes through two-meter-long slide blocks. It took a long time and a lot of effort to get such a job done well; but what struck me was that performing this operation with a drilling machine meant that all the steel cut away was wasted. This hurt me, for in the Soviet Union I'd seen this job done with a hollow cutter that simply bit through the block and pulled out a cylindrical bar of steel that could be used for something else. So I went to the technical department and suggested using a hollow cutter for the job. They said they were not yet capable of designing and making such a complicated instrument. But I was set on it, so I wrote a poster saying that if the draughtsmen and toolmakers were scared of difficulties, they'd better give us the materials and let the workers have a go. My mates supported me and suggested sticking the poster on the door of the technical department. But nothing happened. So we decided to make it ourselves, and the Party supported our idea.

We had no blueprints and no material to start with. I hunted through the drawing-office files until I found a Soviet blueprint, and we got hold of some worn drills to use for the metal. We got together a group of turners, millers, and drilling-machine operators, and we succeeded—after a good deal of trial and error—in making our cutter. The people in the technical department said "Wonderful! Never thought you'd do it!" It made us workers feel good, for the job on the slide block can now be done in four hours instead of thirty, it can be done by one worker instead of three, and he can tend two machines at the same time. The job is smooth and accurate, and we have those fine bars of steel for other purposes. Once again I thought, how right the Party is—if you use your initiative and rely on those around you, you can overcome any difficulties.

Shortly after this, our factory's Communist Party committee called on all the workers in the plant to follow my example. I was overcome with emotion; I had done so little to deserve such praise and honor. The secretary of the provincial Party committee invited me for a talk. I shall never forget what he told me: "Keep it up, but don't get conceited or complacent. On the other hand, don't ever lose faith in your own ability and that of your workmates." This reminded me of my mistakes in the past and I resolved that with the Party's help I would put all I had into my work.

In the autumn of 1958, our factory swung into the Great Leap Forward and production zoomed from forty-two machines a year to two hundred. I was transferred to a new department where there were several problems needing adjustment. One that was creating a bottleneck was connected with the making of a very big and very accurate worm gear; the tools for cutting the worm were not really adequate and the turners were wearing themselves out trying to keep pace with their quota. I thought to myself: "The Party sent me to the Soviet Union to study. Everyone believes in me, and the job is urgent. How shall I tackle it?" I asked the turners to stay behind after work that night, and the three of us sat around the lathe and puzzled over the problems until midnight. We decided that the whole operation should be rearranged, with a new cutting tool based on the principle of an external-winding milling-cutter that could be rotated very fast. We had never seen such a tool and we could not find any reference to it in the textbooks. The leadership, however, gave us great encouragement and sent a man from the drawing office to help us make the blueprints. He worked day and night on them and made several valuable suggestions himself. I saw that the Party's idea of bringing technicians and workers together on a job is very sound.

The first few trials failed, and we still had not got the new cutter working satisfactorily when I had to leave to attend a provincial conference of Activists of Socialist Construction. While I was there, I heard an inspiring report by a peasant called Li Ta-kuei, who had found a most original way of getting water up a mountainside. I thought: "If he can overcome such huge difficulties, surely I can solve my problem." I didn't wait for the end of the conference but went straight back to the plant, determined to stick at it until the new cutter worked properly.

After a few more experiments with the speed, we got it right. The new method was over ten times more efficient than before, and it was fine to see the turners standing upright at the lathe instead of bending over as they had done before. Later we improved it still further.

Last year, 1959, we celebrated the tenth anniversary of our People's Republic. The Great Leap Forward continued. The Party committee at our plant called on all the workers to try and double their output for 1958. The idea caught on, but pretty soon we were held up because of lack of materials. The Party then suggested a campaign to combine raised production with economy, so we concentrated on streamlining designing and working methods.

The Party branch asked me to give practical leadership in the campaign. One idea I hit on was really a very ordinary one. It consisted of hanging up a piece of cloth to prevent scraps of zinc alloy, which is a very soft metal, from flying in all directions like grapeshot during the cutting process. The worker who had to use this metal found he could instantly increase the speed of his machine from 400 to 1,200 revolutions per minute.

Our chief task, as the Party pointed out, was to help everyone improve his technique. In our section there was a newly formed work team consisting entirely of women. Most of them were apprentices and only a few were skilled workers, so their general level made it difficult for them to fulfill their quotas. Some of the men doubted whether women could handle the jobs they were doing, and the girls themselves didn't have much confidence. So I asked if I could help. At first I think I rather frightened them. For example, I warned one girl that the blouse she was wearing was too fancy. She wouldn't listen, and the next day it got caught in a machine. Then I really scolded her, and she went round telling people I had scared her. After that I took care to be patient, explaining in great detail why certain things should be done in certain ways and demonstrating over and over again until the girls got the hang of it. Some of them were nervous when they first tried high-speed drilling, but they all mastered it in the end, and the multiple-tool cutting method too. From then on, their team overfilled its quota every month.

In July, I went with several other advanced workers on a tour of factories in Hupeh province, where we showed and explained our special techniques and learned those of others. This was a very rewarding experience. At one factory I gave three demonstrations of the high-speed thread-cutting method, and before I left, all the lathe operators had raised their speed from 100 to 1,200 rpm.

Not long ago, someone asked me how many technical innovations I've made during these last few years. I couldn't think what to say—those things don't belong to me personally. Whatever I've achieved is due primarily to the help of the Party and my workmates. I owe everything to them. We're all working to help our country build socialism in the shortest possible time. Any worker worth his salt, as soon as he grasps something new, is eager to teach it to those around him. I intend to keep doing that.

A commune work team led by its pace-setter

STUBBORN OX NIU

[The government in Peking can make all sorts of elaborate plans for modernizing and industrializing the Chinese economy, but in the long run it is the bulk of the population—the peasants—who make this development possible. Without their cooperation, the Communists could achieve nothing.

What kind of people are the Chinese peasants? How have they responded to Communism? Chinese literature, because it is largely about life in the countryside, can help us answer these questions.

Take "Stubborn Ox Niu," for example—a story that appeared in *Chinese Literature* magazine in 1960. It is a study of one old peasant and his reactions to different varieties of leadership. It is set in 1958, the year of the Great Leap Forward. This was a period of feverish activity in the rural areas. Not only was there a campaign to decentralize industry; there was also an upswing in the tendency for peasants to pool their individual plots into co-operatives. This process had started in a small way, with spontaneous sharing of tools and draft animals; it had grown rapidly into a massive movement, which the Party used as the basis for the nationwide creation of People's Communes.

Those who imagine that the communization of land was carried out by force or by edict from above underestimate the character of the Chinese peasant. There is a tendency in the West to think of the Chinese as pawns pushed around by doctrinaire Party officials. This view is contradicted by those who have spent time in the Chinese countryside. They know that the peasant is far from docile and that unless the government had patiently explained—to millions of Stubborn Ox Niu's—the advantages of collectivization, it could never have been achieved.

Stubborn Ox Niu is certainly nobody's fool. He is pigheaded but has that strength of will common to peasants everywhere—the quality that has ensured their survival as a class throughout the vicissitudes of history. Even the Communist Party secretary of his co-op cannot tell him what to do and has to use all his tact to handle him at all.

Stubborn Ox is also frank. He is not afraid to speak out against corrupt or weak officials, whether they are Communists or not. And, though it hurts him, he is humble. When he sees that he has been wrong, then—but only then—he is prepared to admit his mistakes. In short, he is without cynicism, genuine, and direct, a "rough diamond" very like those once common in our own rural areas.

Needless to say, he is a very useful man. He is devoted to farming; he loves the land and is capable of immense physical labor to make it productive. Yet he is no mere country bumpkin. He is, in his own way, an expert. He knows the local soil, weather, crops, water, and people better than any university graduate. He is farmer, agronomist, hydrologist, surveyor, and engineer rolled into one. He is also something of a poet.

This is the kind of material the Communists have to work with—a wise people in many ways but a prickly people—a people who respond badly to dogmatic leadership but who give themselves totally to leaders they trust.

Mao Tse-tung knew them well, for he himself was of peasant stock. His dictum that the Party must "serve the people" was an act of faith in the Chinese peasants, and one he knew they would repay a hundredfold.]

A shadowy figure on the mountain path that wound through the trees, he came into sharper focus as he drew nearer. Tall and thin, dressed completely in black, his face a deep bronze color, he was a peasant in his fifties. His hair was tousled; his eyes, under the heavy brows, were burning. He appeared agitated. Leaning slightly forward, head down, he kept his eyes on the path ahead, as if afraid he might stumble. But he looked like the kind of fellow who would keep going until he reached his destination.

His name was Niu Chin-chin. In the old society, he had always been desperately poor. As a young man he had been a lively comical fellow who sang with gusto arias from the local operas. They say his wife used to join him in duets. But after this carefree young man had assumed the burden of married life and worked as a tenant farmer for several years, he stopped singing. Ten more years of tenant farming, and he turned irritable and stubborn.

One autumn, they had a bad harvest. Niu didn't even gather enough rice to feed his family through the winter. The landlord kept coming around for the rent. At first Niu explained and pleaded for an abatement. Then he began to stiffen.

"With soil like this, you couldn't bring in a good harvest?" scoffed the landlord. "Who can believe that?"

"With a fine concubine like yours, you couldn't produce a son?" retorted Niu. "Who can believe that?"

"I'll send you up to the county, you lout! You'll sit in jail!"

"I was worried what I was going to do about food. In jail at least I won't starve. Please get me committed quickly!"

"Impudent wretch! Is there nothing you fear on earth or in heaven?"

"Even death doesn't scare me, Your Honor. Set your mind at ease!"

"You can't be budged by fire or water, you . . . you stubborn ox!"

"Thanks for the nickname, Your Honor," said Niu, bowing deeply.

When bluster couldn't frighten him, the landlord took harsher methods. He sent a gang to beat him up. Though bleeding and exhausted, he wouldn't beg for mercy. One soft word might have made the gang let up. But a sign of weakness from Niu—try and get it!

Having his harvests snatched by landlords year after year, Stubborn Ox Niu moved from village to village. He finally settled down for good in Dry Gulch. High and arid, with poor soil, Dry Gulch raised wet rice, although the sole source of water was the rain that fell from the sky. Only a man with the strength and stubbornness of an ox could stick it out there. But, because local rents were slightly lower, it was possible to scrape through a year if you were lucky enough to get an early rainfall.

Niu, his wife, and their half-grown son worked day and night, turning the ground into neat paddy fields. They ploughed deep and applied plenty of fertilizer. But because there was no rain in early spring, the rice shoots were transplanted late and the yield was poor. Although rainfall may have been irregular, the landlord never failed to call for his rent on time. He arrived as soon as the rice was gathered.

"When will you deliver my share of the harvest?"

"There isn't enough here for us to eat. We'll talk about the rent later."

"What are you up to?"

"Nothing. This is all the rice there is. You can look at it, but you can't take it."

"You talk as if the land belonged to you!"

"It isn't mine, but I've worked it for a couple of years. If you take our food away, you can till the land yourself!"

The landlord looked at Niu and he looked at the cleanly gleaned fields. He knew that Niu loved the soil and that he'd never get another tenant like him.

"All right, then, see what you can do."

"If you're leaving it up to me, I'm going to fill my family's bellies first."

"You stubborn ox! You can't be budged by fire or water, can you?"

After Liberation, Stubborn Ox retained his nickname, but he gave no displays of his well-known trait. He showed so much initiative during the land reform that the comrade in charge of the land reform team was thinking of introducing him into membership of the Communist Party. But Niu wouldn't agree. "I've got the wrong temperament for a Communist," he said. "I'm too obstinate. When another fellow makes a mistake, he can admit it. Not me. Even when I know I'm wrong, I can't bring myself to say it. That sort of Communist would only be a burden to the Party."

Life became steadily better. Niu had no big worries, and was happy. In the ten years following Liberation, he gave vent to his stubbornness only twice.

Once was when the elementary farming co-ops were formed. Niu joined in with his share of land. He also took part in the higher type of co-ops when they were organized. In 1957, when a few members of the co-op alleged they weren't getting enough grain, Niu's stubborn streak flared up.

Hsieh Lin, the vice-chairman of the co-op, was inciting the members to demand a larger share of the grain harvest. At a meeting of the entire co-op, Wang Chang-hai, formerly a well-to-do peasant, brought a jug of pickled vegetables and set it down in the center of the township government courtyard where the meeting was being held. Wang's wife wept and said that was all they had left to eat. A few people followed their lead and bemoaned their "hardships."

A pall seemed to settle over the gathering. After the moaners had finished their complaints, Hsieh Lin turned to Niu and asked: "How much grain is your family short?"

His eyes bulging with suppressed rage, Niu pushed his way

through the crowd and took his stand beside the jug of pickled vegetables.

"My family has enough to eat," he said. "We're not short of anything!"

"Oho!" people whispered, "he's going to get obstinate again."

"That's strange. Everybody else is short of grain, but your family—"

Niu didn't let him finish. Scowling, he cut in, "What's strange about it? If we're not short, we're not short! When this co-op started, everyone agreed to a share of 400 catties per person. But some people are eating four meals a day and having another snack before going to bed! Some people are even selling grain to buy wine! That's why some are short of grain. And you're a fine vice-chairman, Hsieh Lin! You don't investigate to see if there's a real shortage; you just take it for granted and want to know how much! All I can say is: You're on the wrong track!"

Turning, he gave the jug a kick and sent it rolling across the courtyard.

Hsieh Lin shook a finger at him and yelled, "You're trying to break up the meeting! You're preventing democratic discussion! Comrades, are we going to let him get away with that?"

But none of the peasants rose to the vice-chairman's bait. In the silence that followed, Stubborn Ox angrily stamped out.

The next evening he again attended the meeting. Hsieh Lin demanded that he publicly criticize himself. A handful of peasants (those who had been alleging they were short of grain) sided with the vice-chairman. Frightened and weeping, Niu's wife tried to pull him back into the crowd, but he pushed forward and strode to the foot of the speaker's platform. Pointing at the vice-chairman, he shouted: "So you want me to criticize myself, do you? Let me tell you, Hsieh

Lin, you've picked the wrong man! I never gave in to the reactionaries, and now that the people have taken power I certainly won't give in to bad leadership! If I ever criticize myself, it won't be before you! In the future, we'll see who has to make a self-criticism!"

Standing off to one side, Niu's wife was trembling with fear. If her son, Niu Hsin, had raised such a row, she would have promptly slapped him. But what could she do with this obstinate old man?

Finally she succeeded in dragging him from the meeting place.

The third night, he went again. People struggle for justice as a fish fights for water. Stubborn Ox Niu was not the man to run from a battle. This time he found the atmosphere quite different. Presiding over the meeting was the vice-secretary of the county Party committee. Hsieh Lin, looking very pale and deflated, sat with his head down as if afraid to face anyone. The peasants who had squawked so loudly about the grain two days before were also much subdued, and hid themselves in the rear.

Speaking at the meeting this evening were people of a different type. They spoke truthfully and to the point, and every one of them mentioned Stubborn Ox Niu. They all said his view was correct.

The final opinion of the majority was that there was no shortage of grain.

The second time the old man got angry was after the Great Leap Forward began in the countryside.

Stubborn Ox had a rich store of farming experience. But, working all his life on poor soil, he had never had a chance to develop his talent fully. This made him unhappy. Whenever he heard about other production brigades increasing their output, his whole body would burn. But try as he might, tilling the arid ground of Dry Gulch, he could never catch up.

In 1958, when the Great Leap began, a production goal

was set of 1,000 catties per *mu*. Old Niu thought and thought, and came to the conclusion that even if he worked himself to death, he could not squeeze a thousand catties out of a *mu* of Dry Gulch land. After several days of mental agony, he said to his son, "We can't live here any longer. This soil is dead. No matter how you strive, it's all in vain."

Startled, his son said, "What do you want to do?"

"A thousand catties is not that much, really. But you can't get it here. If we can't keep up with the Great Leap, it'll be an awful loss of face. So I was thinking, we ought to move over to your married sister's co-op. They have good land, and they're short of people."

"But how can we do that? She's on a different co-op. Even if this one let us go, that one mighn't want us."

"They do. I've already asked."

"Suppose our co-op won't release us?"

"We'll go anyway!"

"You're getting senile, old man!" said his wife when she heard. "We've been living here twenty-five years. How could you have the heart to leave?"

"Why not? These past few days there hasn't been enough water to give the ox a decent drink. In another few days, you'll be able to see the bottom of the well. Who wants to stay here?"

He went to see Li Ho-ping, Party secretary of the co-op. The secretary was on the phone, making notes as he talked. He had bushy hair, a round face, a prominent nose, and thick lips. He spoke in a slow, unruffled manner.

"Ah, Uncle Niu. Not busy today?" he asked, as he hung up the phone.

"Comrade Li, I have a request. I want to move."

"What? When did you get that idea?"

"Just recently." Niu coughed. "After the Great Leap started."

"But how could you bear to leave our little Dry Gulch? Is there any particular reason?"

"Yes. Dry Gulch has no water. It's impossible to make a Great Leap Forward here." The old man sat down on a stool opposite the secretary.

"We're planning to build a reservoir in the mountains. We'll have water here soon."

"Can't be done," said the old man positively. "It can't be done."

"Why not?"

"One co-op doesn't have enough manpower to undertake such a project. And even if we did, we'd be spending an enormous sum to irrigate a small piece of ground. Anyhow, there are no springs in these mountains. The reservoir would be empty. We'd be a laughing-stock. . . . I'm fifty-three. I've never had a year when everything went well on the land I was working. I'm getting on in years, and now there's this Great Leap. I want to try some place else, some place where I can concentrate everything on raising a good crop. What's wrong with that?"

"Uncle, you're just making excuses for yourself."

"Am I? All I know is that even a god couldn't get a bumper harvest out of this ground! Ah, Comrade Secretary, that 1,000-catty target makes my mouth water. But when I look at this Dry Gulch land, all the strength goes out of me!" He spread his hands and sighed.

"Where were you thinking of moving?"

"To my daughter's place. Their land's near a lake. If we use our heads, we'll harvest 1,500 to 2,000 catties per *mu*, easy!" He clenched his fists so tightly that his fingers cracked.

"But somebody has to till Dry Gulch." Comrade Li's calm voice quickened a bit.

"Whoever wants to till it can go ahead! Not me! For twenty-five years I was ready to irrigate this land with my spit, if it would have done any good! It's not easy for me to leave here, Comrade Secretary. . . ." There was a quaver in the old man's voice.

"You mustn't go. They're a co-op and so are we. If you

leave, we'll be losing three able-bodied members! You mustn't go!"

"I only want to raise output. I don't care which co-op I do it in!" Stubborn Ox retorted, his breath whistling through his nostrils—a sure sign that he was getting worked up. "Wherever I am, I work for a living. No one has to support me!"

Comrade Li knew that once Niu decided to do anything, nine oxen and two tigers couldn't drag him back. But he felt badly. "Why does he want to move to another co-op?" he wondered. If it had been anyone else, he would not have been so upset. But the old man was not only a good, honest person with determination and courage; he also had a kind of ingrained loyalty to the Party and to the cause of socialism. Usually taciturn, if anything concerning the Party or socialism was involved, he would rise and speak out fearlessly, criticizing anyone he thought wrong, regardless of position or rank. He had no formal understanding of political analysis or practice; he acted entirely on the basis of his class instincts. He was a true, down-to-earth poor peasant.

Ever since the formation of the co-op, he had been a model farmer. He was in his element enthusiastically toiling in the fields. In half a lifetime of scrabbling in the poor soil of Dry Gulch, he had come to understand it thoroughly—when to plough and plant, how to select seeds, dig irrigation ditches, control insect pests, fight drought, prevent floods, improve the soil; he had learned these things from his own personal experience. In the past few years, at every spring planting and at every autumn harvest, Comrade Li had sought his advice, treasuring him as a virtual living encyclopedia of agricultural lore. From the bottom of his heart, he did not want him to go.

But, since things had come to such a pass, there was no point in trying to compel the old man to remain.

"All right," he said with a sigh, "I consent to you and your family moving. But you may regret it one day, Old Uncle. Leaving is easy, but it's hard to return. When you're sorry, it'll be too late."

"I'll never be sorry! Never! I'm leaving because I want to— of my own free will." Pleased and smiling, Old Niu said, "A real man does a thing thoroughly or not at all. I'll never want to come back! But I'll never forget you folks, or little Dry Gulch either!" He wagged his head, and his face was tinged with sorrow.

"Don't move away, then. Ah, we hate to part with you!"

"Impossible! My bow is drawn."

"You can't be budged by fire or water. You really are an old stubborn ox!" Comrade Li cried, shaking his finger under the old man's nose. It was the first time he had ever used this name.

Old Niu chuckled. "That was what the landlord called me! Curse away—you know I won't get angry with you."

The next morning, Old Niu and his family departed from Dry Gulch.

The co-op lent him another ox cart to help him move, and his son-in-law arrived with a horse and cart. As soon as the horse cart was loaded—with trunks and cupboards covered over with rice straw—the son-in-law shouted to the horse and it started off at a trot.

When the ox cart also was loaded, the old couple stood gazing sadly around the empty courtyard. After all, it had been their home for many years. Finally, they said good-bye to the friends and neighbors who had come to see them off. Niu Hsin drove, Mama sat on top of the load, Old Niu walked behind. Slowly, they left the village.

Rolling along the embankment between the fields, the cart proceeded toward the pass at the southern end of the gulch. Most of the narrow paddy fields had already been dug out in preparation for the spring planting, and the soil steamed in the sun. In the undug fields were cracks a span wide, like mouths open to the heavens, begging for water. White stones flashed on the river flats. Along the banks, the slim leaves of the straight, glistening reeds were motionless in the faint spring breeze, as if enervated by the warmth of the sun. Except for the green cactus plants spotting the slopes, the entire gulch was brown and dry.

At the top of the pass the cart halted to give the ox a breather. Old Niu turned and looked back at the gulch, at his old home amid the trees.

"We're leaving, little gulch," he said. "You gave us happiness and you gave us hardship over the years. . . . We're not leaving because we want to get rich. We want to make a Great Leap Forward. Please forgive us. Don't be angry. Birds always fly to the light, don't they? So don't hate us. Let's part on good terms."

Mama Niu was already very depressed. Now, hearing her husband's words, she burst into tears. They'd been married for thirty years. Even when they'd gone into hiding to avoid the landlord's debt collectors, she had never seen Niu so downcast.

Not long after they had moved to Lucky Co-op, they heard that their old co-op—the Pine Tree—was preparing to build a reservoir next to the gulch. Old Niu was excited, but he couldn't believe it. One co-op simply didn't have the manpower to undertake such a big engineering project.

But when the rice sprouts were planted, the news was confirmed. Pine Tree Co-op was really going ahead with it. Old Niu was about to go and see for himself, when the county telephoned and asked Lucky Co-op to prepare a field demonstration. Lucky had done a fine job of planting and its sprouts were growing exceptionally well. The authorities wanted other co-ops in the county to learn from their experience.

At the field demonstration, Old Niu met Comrade Li. The Party secretary told him they had already stopped work on the reservoir because they were short of men, materials, and technique. "But we're definitely going to build it," Li assured him. "If not this year, then next. You'll see."

Old Niu only smiled.

When the grain heads were heavy and drooping, all over the country co-ops began combining into People's Communes. Old Niu heard that work on the reservoir at Dry Gulch had been resumed. At first it seemed to him that the communes were too large, that they tried to handle too much, that they had been organized too quickly. He was soon going to learn their advantages. If four co-ops had not merged into one commune, the Dry Gulch dam would not have been completed by the time he became a grandfather—and his son Niu Hsin still didn't even have a sweetheart.

Work on the dam started and stopped, started and stopped again, Old Niu's heart rising and falling with it. "What would the soil in Dry Gulch be like if it could be irrigated?" he wondered. "But that's impossible. There are no streams in those mountains. Just relying on rain water won't do any good. Even if you could accumulate a little water behind a dam, the sun would dry it up before the next spring planting. . . ."

In spite of his doubts, he couldn't get the project out of his mind. Physically, he was in the Lucky Co-op, but his heart was still in Dry Gulch. The dam was his. How could he stand idly by?

One day, pretending that he had to go to town, he asked for the day off. Then he headed for his former home. Following a small path, he climbed the western mountain. He could see the little village nestling among the trees. He intended to detour around it, afraid of meeting old neighbors, who might ask, "Have you come back?" But somehow his steps led him directly to his old house. To his surprise, he found it empty, the door sealed. In the courtyard were piles of recently harvested rice. A black dog, lying on the ground, rose and rushed up to him. It sniffed his clothes, then wagged its tail. It didn't bark. "It recognizes me," Old Niu thought. Everything in the compound looked the same, all neat and clean. "Can they be keeping it for me?" he wondered.

In the fields outside the village, the rice had just been cut and fresh sprouts were rising from the original roots. The whole little river valley was a pale green. He had never seen it look so beautiful. . . . What would it be like with irrigation?

He left the village. Rounding the mountain, he entered the pass and halted in amazement. The labor forces of all the four former co-ops were swarming over the slopes. Excavated earth flew by on overhead trolleys and on improvised wooden rails; below, ox carts, horse carts, wheelbarrows, and baskets on shoulder-poles were in action. People were digging, transporting, singing, laughing, shouting. They were splitting open the mountain, rocks were tumbling, a pall of dust rose to the skies, then rained down on your clothes. . . .

He wound his way through the masses of people, climbed to a rocky ledge on the mountain side, and gazed around. He was afraid he would meet an old friend who would say: "See how strong our commune is!"

The next morning, just as Comrade Li was washing his face, Niu Hsin came in. "You're up early," said Comrade Li. "And you've already covered twelve miles."

"You don't know the half of it! The old man got me out of bed at the crack of dawn. He wants me to tell you two things. First, don't try to turn all the soil before planting the beans. It's too late for that. Turn as much as you can, but the main thing is to get the beans in fast. Where the ground's too dry, you can moisten it a bit. Second, he says your stone work is no good; the way you're doing it, the dam will collapse with the first big mountain torrent. He says he has a friend in Changchuan who used to be a stonemason. If you want him, he can get him." Niu Hsin pulled out a letter his father had written to the stonemason and handed it to the Party secretary. It read:

BIG BROTHER WU,

I haven't seen or heard from you in three years. Are you still alive? You can't be dead. I'm not dead either. If we haven't died yet, this certainly isn't the time to do it. If you're still alive, and not sick, don't get sick whatever you do. I want you to come out to Dry Gulch and give us a hand. You must come. If you don't, I'll curse you. You don't know—we're parched out here! Must close now. Will give you the details when we meet. There are a lot of them. Even in ten full days and nights, I won't be able to tell you the full story.

YOUNGER BROTHER NIU

The Party secretary laughed, then grabbed Niu Hsin by the shoulders and rocked him from side to side.

"Your dad hasn't forgotten Dry Gulch! All right, young-ster, go and get the mason."

"If you get the dam built, I think the old man will be so happy he'll want to come back."

"You mean it?"

The boy laughed. "You know what he's like. If he gets the urge to do something, a flaming volcano couldn't stop him."

After breakfast, Niu Hsin set out. The following evening, he returned with a man in his sixties, a thin man with a long beard. When the newcomer learned that Old Niu had moved to Lucky Co-op, he was furious.

"He drags me all the way out here after he's already moved away! I never thought he'd pull such a dirty trick, the old scoundrel! Niu Hsin, I blame you for this, too! Why didn't you tell me you'd left Dry Gulch?"

"I was afraid you wouldn't come," the boy replied honestly.

"Old Uncle," said Secretary Li, "in the old days a whole county couldn't build a dam. Today, this commune is going to build one by itself. We're inviting you to be our chief stone-worker. Please help us out."

The old man was very moved. Stroking his beard, he thought for a moment. Then he replied:

Building an irrigation canal to carry
melted snow from the mountains . . .

"What you say sounds good. I'll do it. But I don't look a
bit like a worker in this long beard. Off with it!"

He had Comrade Li shave him clean.

The old man was an excellent stonemason. Although he
had not worked at his trade for many years and his hands
trembled a little and he wasn't as strong as he used to be, he
shaped stone blocks quickly and well. As he worked, he
trained apprentices. By the time the job was done, he had
trained nineteen young stonemasons of the Pine Tree Commune.

Behind the mountain east of the dam ran a small, clear
stream. Inasmuch as Dry Gulch had no water, why not cut a
tunnel through the mountain and lead the stream into the
reservoir? With the old craftsman clambering over the cliffs
and selecting the most likely spot, a tunnel was soon bored
through.

After the reservoir was completed, Old Niu invited Big
Brother Wu to his home, and the two old friends drank to-

gether. "Here's to you, Big Brother!" said Stubborn Ox Niu. "I thank you on behalf of the Pine Tree Commune."

Old Wu drained his cup and thumped it down on the table. "You're a member of Lucky Commune," he shouted. "What right do you have to speak for Pine Tree?"

"Don't ask, old rascal! I must confess," Stubborn Ox groaned, "that I still think of myself as belonging to the Pine Tree Commune."

"Aha, you wretch! Aren't you full of nasty schemes?"

As they were drinking, a man came to invite Old Wu to the county Party committee. Old Niu rode with them in the jeep as far as the office of the Pine Tree Commune. After they dropped him off, he went in to see Secretary Li.

"I've come to ask you a favor," said Old Niu, as he entered the door. "I want to move back to Dry Gulch."

"What's that you say?" Comrade Li feigned deafness.

"I said I want to move back to Dry Gulch," Stubborn Ox shouted, his face red.

"Don't you remember what I told you when you were moving away, Old Uncle? Working in a commune isn't like paying social calls, coming and going as you please." Comrade Li tweaked his eyebrow to keep himself from laughing.

"What are you talking about? This has nothing to do with social calls! I made a mistake, that's true. But no one has eyes in the back of his head. You know very well: 'Every

. . . through the desert to new farm lands

man makes mistakes, unless he's a god; every horse makes mistakes, unless it's a dragon.' Chairman Mao says we ought to forgive a man who takes the wrong road, provided he's willing to turn back. Let me return to Dry Gulch and I promise to produce not 1,000 catties per *mu* but 1,200. What do you say? I'll give you a written guarantee!"

This was exactly what Comrade Li had been hoping for, but he didn't agree at once. When he had let old Stubborn Ox leave Dry Gulch, he had regretted it later. Now he wanted to take this opportunity to cure the old man of his capriciousness.

"You'll have to get permission in writing from Lucky Commune," he said. "If they agree, we can consider it. If they don't, it would create bad feelings between the two communes if we took you back."

Old Stubborn Ox was not at all happy, but he couldn't refuse. Without Comrade Li's consent, he wouldn't be able to get back.

"How official we're getting!" he snorted.

He hurried back to Lucky Commune. Secretary Chang's reply was the same as Comrade Li's:

"If you want to move back, first get permission from Pine Tree."

"Ha! How official we're getting!"

The next day, he hastened back to Pine Tree Commune. The result was the same.

In three days, he shuttled back and forth between the two communes three times. Agitated and depressed, he had a bellyful of anger to which he did not dare give vent. The third time he arrived at Pine Tree Commune, he shouted at Secretary Li: "I can't stand any more of this! Do you want me to hang myself?" He yanked off his hat and mopped his perspiring head. Wearily, he sank down on a bench and sat drooping, like a miserable child.

"All right. Never mind the letter of permission. But you'll have to criticize yourself before the members."

Old Stubborn Ox leaped up as if he had been stabbed, gazing at the secretary in utter shock. Then, flinging his hand down in a gesture of rejection, he stalked out without a word.

But early the next morning Niu Hsin arrived, chuckling. "The old man insists I explain to you that he doesn't know how to make a self-criticism."

"Go back and tell him that unless he criticizes himself, the members won't accept him into the commune. Not only must he criticize himself—he must do it thoroughly."

On January 20, 1959, Pine Tree held a meeting of all its members to discuss measures for a big leap in the spring planting. Sure enough, old Stubborn Ox showed up.

The discussion had finished and the meeting had quieted down when he entered. Comrade Li addressed the members. He said that Niu Chin-chin had requested to return to Dry Gulch. The Party committee thought he should criticize himself. If he did it well, and if the members agreed he should come back, he would be allowed.

"Uncle Niu, you can begin."

Comrade Li withdrew and Stubborn Ox came forward. His arms wrapped around his chest, his eyes on his feet, he turned awkwardly this way and that. Then, raising his head, he stammered:

"Neighbors, I was wrong. I shouldn't have left Dry Gulch. I ask you to let me come back—not as a social caller, but to work together with you all. Among the old operas, there's one called 'The Prodigal Son Returns.' I'm your prodigal son. A prodigal son returns when he wants to mend his ways. So you ought to accept him. When I was a young man, I used to like to sing. Before I criticize myself, I want to sing a ballad:

"Fifty-five this year
Is Old Niu called Chin-chin.

He wanted to leap forward,
But got his head in a spin.

" 'Dry Gulch is no good,' said he,
'Its fields are always dry.'
Ignoring the secretary's urging,
He decided he would fly.

"No faith in the strength of the communes,
No faith in the people's vim.
No dam could be built in Dry Gulch,
That's how it seemed to him.

"Oh, I couldn't see the truth,
Though it was right before my eyes.
I'm longing to come home now,
I must apologize.

"Yes, I made a mistake,
Old neighbors, forgive.
Please let me return,
To Dry Gulch and live.

"I'll listen to the Party,
I'll work with might and main,
And never let my stubbornness
Run away with me again!"

That Old Stubborn Ox was willing to criticize himself at all was remarkable enough. But to do it in verse—that was piling wonder on wonder! His listeners rocked with laughter. They shouted: "Good! Excellent!" "You needn't criticize yourself any further!" "We'll help you move!"

As Old Stubborn Ox came down the western slope once more, his family's belongings were piled on three ox carts.

Mama Niu rode on the last one. Old Niu walked behind. As they rolled through the pass, the old man halted.

"Little Dry Gulch, we've come back," he said. "I owe you an apology—but I've already criticized myself."

Mama Niu didn't cry this time. She laughed.

A YOUNG TIGER

[So far we have emphasized the serious side of China—the sufferings of the people and their efforts to eliminate the injustice that had plagued them for so long.

In case the reader should get the idea that China is all work and no play, we turn now to something in a lighter vein: the subject of national fitness. Sport, in particular, because of its role in improving a people's physical and mental health, must be considered an integral part of the process of nation-building.

Western sports are comparatively new in China, but they have caught on like wildfire. At the same time, many old Chinese sports have been revived. The government has promoted this development, not only because sport makes people fit but also because it is a source of challenge and pleasure and teaches the values of teamwork and discipline.

The most popular sports in China today are the cheapest—games like table tennis, volleyball, and basketball, which can be set up with a minimum of equipment. Table tennis is the national obsession. It is a common sight in the cities and in the villages to see children whacking away at a ball with homemade bats, on a table constructed out of bits of board, with a piece of string or a bamboo stick for a net. Nor is it rare for a foreign visitor to be trounced by a ten-year-old who can barely see over the table!

Some Chinese sports are frankly military in nature.

Instead of throwing the shot-put, the Chinese throw dummy grenades. Instead of a paper chase or cross-country run, they prefer map-reading or walkie-talkie excursions. This combination of sport and military training is not a Chinese innovation; some of our own sports—javelin and discus, archery, fencing, shooting—are equally warlike. It is interesting to note, however, that sports involving violent contact—boxing is the best example—have been outlawed since the Communists came to power.

Perhaps the most famous athlete the new China has produced is Chuang Tse-tung, who won the World Table Tennis Championship several times. The article that follows is taken from a 1965 issue of *China's Sports* and describes how Chuang, still a teenager, won his first international title.

As a piece of reporting on sport, it is not so different from Western journalism. The writer stresses the arduous training, the strict self-discipline, the ability to receive criticism, the courage, the dedication to team and country—qualities that any international champion needs.

But there are differences too. An American athlete would not look down from the plane taking him off to the championships and say: "Down there my people are toiling in the factories and on the farms to raise production. I must do my bit for the Great Leap Forward."

Nor would an American feel that his prowess in sport was merely the reflection of a national morale, a new spirit of altruistic service that everyone—not just a champion—was expected to cultivate.

These differences are important, for they have contributed to the development of a uniquely Chinese style. In table tennis, this takes the form of relentless, close-in smashes and dogged defense, with lightning variations to confuse the opponent. Perhaps it should be called the "guerrilla" style, for it must have been something similar that tied down the Japanese armies and outmaneuvered Chiang Kai-shek.]

STORMY NIGHT

Heavy clouds scudded before the wind in a leaden morning sky. Thunder crashed and the rain soon came pouring down in torrents. Throughout the day, the storm's fury mounted. The streets were flooded; trolley and bus services came to a standstill. This was a cloudburst such as Peking had rarely seen.

That evening, Chuang Tse-tung gazed anxiously from the sky to the clock, from the clock to the sky. It was half past six. Hurriedly knotting his red Young Pioneer's scarf, he wrapped up his table tennis bat, rolled his trousers above his knees, and snatched an umbrella.

"Where are you going in this rain?" called his mother.

*Hsiao** Chung paused.

"To the Children's Palace."

"What? In this weather? You'd better stay home."

"How can I? According to our regulations, we practice at half past seven."

"Regulations or no regulations, you can make an exception today. There'll be no one there, anyway."

Hsiao Chuang replied with adult seriousness:

"Mother, what kind of athlete will I be if I stop training just because it rains?"

Seeing that her son was adamant, the mother let him go with a warning to be careful on the way.

The instructor stood at a window in the Children's Palace, staring at the stormy sky through the streaming panes. Surely no one would turn up on such a night!

Thunder rolled and a streak of lightning split the sky. In its blinding glare, he saw the figure of a boy at the gate, sloshing through the puddles and bracing a large red umbrella against the driving wind and rain. Hurrying to the door to meet him, he saw that it was *Hsiao* Chuang.

* *Hsiao*, meaning "little" or "young," is placed before a Chinese surname as a form of endearment.

"I didn't expect you to come in this rain!"

"Why not? We've got a training session this evening."

The instructor was moved. Gazing at Chuang Tse-tung, who was dripping from head to foot, he said with emotion:

"You've done the right thing! An athlete should make strict demands on himself and consciously practice discipline. You've got the right spirit. Now dry yourself off. We'll start on time."

With this kind of perseverance in training, Chuang Tse-tung improved rapidly. Within two years, he had won the Peking Junior Singles Championship three times and had placed third in the men's singles.

THE DEBUT

One day in early summer, 1958, the Peking Gymnasium was the scene of a grueling competition between the Chinese team and the visiting Hungarian team, then the strongest in Europe. The weather was not particularly warm, but *Hsiao* Chuang was perspiring. Beads of sweat broke out on his face and arms, although he kept toweling himself.

This was the sixteen-year-old boy's first international competition. His opponent was to be Gyetval, European runner-up and Hungarian national champion. Nervous and restless, Chuang Tse-tung stood at the players' entrance and peered around the packed gym. From the sea of spectators there arose a deafening roar. He had been here before to watch competitions, but never had the gym seemed so huge and the crowd so large. He was soon to go in as a representative of the Peking table tennis team. How would he make out? He felt terribly ill at ease.

The team captain and the coach came up. "Well, young fellow, you'll be in there playing in a few minutes. Feeling confident?"

Instead of answering, *Hsiao* Chuang frowned.

The team captain gave him a pat on the shoulder. "You

must be brave. You must have the courage to take on famous champions. Don't be nervous. Use all your skill and you'll have every chance of winning!"

His teammates also came over to give him encouragement: "This is your chance to prove yourself. As soon as you get in there, let yourself go and hit as hard as you can. You'll win for sure!"

The loudspeaker announced the next match: Hungarian national champion Gyetval versus Peking junior champion Chuang Tse-tung. Applause rippled through the gym. Preceded by the referees, Gyetval strode on to the court. The coach tapped *Hsiao* Chuang on the arm and said: "Go on! And put everything you've got into it!"

The spectators tittered at the sight of the tall and sturdy Gyetval leaning down to shake hands with the much smaller Chuang Tse-tung. Someone kept shouting: *"Chiayou, Hsiao Chuang!"** Strong and clear, the voice rang in his ears. He drew in his breath and quietly let it out again; new strength seemed to surge through him.

He took up his positon at the table, thinking: "Now's the time to win credit for my country. As a representative of Peking, I mustn't let the people down!" He made an effort to steady his nerves, and his former apprehension vanished. With a sense of responsibility, he tensed himself for the coming battle.

As the match got under way, *Hsiao* Chuang unleashed a series of powerful forehand and backhand smashes. The ball hurtled at his opponent like bullets from a rapid-fire gun. This new, close-range, all-out-attack style of play was something Gyetval had never come across. Kept on the run, he was completely overwhelmed. The game ended in a defeat for the well-known European champion.

The victory came as a big surprise to the spectators, and

* *Chiayou!*, literally "Pour on more oil!" is a phrase of encouragement, like our "come on!"

Chuang Tse-tung, winner of the men's singles at the
26th and 27th World Table Tennis Championships

they congratulated *Hsiao* Chuang with a prolonged ovation.

The team captain greeted him as he walked into the
dressing room. Affectionately ruffling his bristly crew cut, he
remarked: "You see? You played with everything you had
and you beat a champion."

Chuang Tse-tung learned from this tournament that courage and audacity are the first requirements in a contest
against a strong opponent.

YOUR COUNTRY WANTS THAT SET!

The plane took off and gained altitude. Among the passengers was a group of young table tennis players from the
Chinese B team, setting off for a tour of Europe.

Chuang Tse-tung gazed rather wistfully at the green and
gold city of Peking slowly receding into the distance. This
was the first time he would be competing abroad as a representative of his country, and he was beset by mixed emotions.
He felt that matters were no longer so simple; his playing
was now linked with his country's honor. He had been given

a glorious mission, but he realized that it would also be an arduous one.

He recalled what an official of the State Physical Culture and Sports Commission had said to the team before their departure: "You are China's new generation in table tennis. . . . You are going abroad to represent the people of your country. You must play with courage and determination, and strive to win victory and glory for the motherland. Even when the score is against you, do not lose heart. You may not want that set, but your country does!" These words had stuck in *Hsiao* Chuang's mind, and he kept repeating them, savoring their significance.

Far below the plane's wings, where factories poured forth white smoke and broad plains swept from horizon to horizon, the workers of China toiled, the commune members labored to wrest more cotton and grain from the soil. Under the guidance of the Communist Party and Chairman Mao, hundreds of millions of courageous and industrious people were forging ahead with unprecedented determination, raising high the red banner of Mao Tse-tung's thinking. The Great Leap Forward was in progress, and the new generation had to reflect the daring spirit of the people. Good-bye, beloved Peking! Good-bye, beloved motherland! We shall not fail your trust in us. . . .

In England, the people meeting the plane seemed somewhat disappointed at the sight of these young, unknown table tennis players.

Chuang Tse-tung was severely tested in a match at Oxford. He lost the first set to the British star, Bryan Merrett. Halfway through the second set, he was trailing dismally with the score 2–15 against him.

As he walked over to pick up the ball, a voice seemed to whisper: "Even if you don't want this set, your country does!" His heart leapt: We are the first sporting delegation to visit Britain since the founding of New China. Every success and every defeat affects the prestige of our country.

I have no right to throw away a single point! He felt as if his people were standing at his shoulder, watching him with love and encouragement in their eyes. He forced himself to be calm, and one thought drove all others from his mind: I will catch up!

The match continued. Chuang Tse-tung had overcome his jangled nerves. Using top drives, he painstakingly lifted the ball over the net more than twenty times. At last an opportunity came, and he seized it to make a killing smash, winning the point. It required almost superhuman will power for a player of his fast-attacking style to persevere in this kind of play. That one point was a token of his devotion to his people and his sense of responsibility to his country. With a combination of caution and audacity, he slowly but surely made a comeback, eventually leveling the score at 19–19. Perhaps Merrett had never met such a relentless adversary; he got rattled and lost two points in succession. *Hsiao* Chuang had won the set. In the deciding set, he played with even greater determination and confidence. Powerless to stave off his attacks, Merrett went down under a hurricane of smashes.

During their tour of Britain, the young Chinese players performed splendidly, achieving five victories and one draw out of a total of six matches. This created something of a sensation throughout the British Isles. Overseas Chinese who flocked to the games were moved to tears by the successive victories of these youngsters. One old man said: "Watching you spirited, dynamic players is like seeing the motherland reborn. The Chinese were once looked on as the 'Sick Men of the East.' But now they have risen to their feet and they are showing the world their inexhaustible vitality. This makes us proud!" As an expression of their love for their country, the overseas Chinese in the city of Birmingham presented the players with a large pennant bearing the words: "Your Prowess Awes the World."

Hsiao Chuang was again deeply impressed with the great

significance of his calling. Table tennis was much more than a game; it was a revolutionary task, a way of fighting for the revolution.

TO PERSEVERE IS TO WIN

After their British visit, the Chinese players set out for the 5th Scandinavian Table Tennis Championships, 1959. They laughed and talked incessantly during the train journey, still exhilarated by their recent successes. The team captain felt a quiet satisfaction as he watched these lively youngsters. In the middle of an animated conversation, *Hsiao* Chuang suddenly turned to him and asked:

"We've achieved two-thirds of what we came to do, haven't we?"

The team captain gazed at him, wondering. There was an innocent smile on *Hsiao* Chuang's lips, and his eyes were wide and questioning. Instead of replying directly, the team captain told a story about an athlete who went abroad in the days before Liberation. The reactionary Kuomintang Government, he pointed out, would occasionally send people to competitions abroad, but purely as a form of window dressing. It had no genuine concern for their welfare. One such player had found himself short of his return fare after a competition. He had cabled several times for assistance, but the Kuomintang Government did not reply. Finally, the man had to sell his personal belongings. This, plus contributions from some people who took pity on him, enabled him to scrape up enough to return home in the hold of a freighter.

As he listened, *Hsiao* Chuang could not help making a comparison with his own life as a representative of New China, and he felt fortunate indeed. The team captain smiled, and came to the point:

"It isn't by chance that we've attained good results on this trip. We must not let ourselves get complacent. We should carry on with the same spirit as we had in the beginning, especially now that we are nearing the end of the tour. We will not have complete success unless we sustain our efforts to the last."

These words had the sobering effect of a cool spring breeze on *Hsiao* Chuang, enabling him to see things in their proper perspective.

A severe trial still lay ahead of them. The Scandinavian Championships were nominally a North European affair, but in reality it would be a tournament having worldwide dimensions, with a hundred or more top-flight players from three continents—Asia, Europe, and America—taking part.

The championships turned out to be among the most strenuous, hotly contested, and exhausting competitions ever held. On the day of the finals, Chuang Tse-tung played from twelve o'clock noon until almost midnight. By actual count, he had fought a total of ten matches and forty-one sets, with no more than a twenty-minute break between matches. Despite this tremendous strain, three finals still awaited him.

It was time to start again. The crucial moment had arrived, the moment to win honor for his country. Perseverance! Licking his parched lips, *Hsiao* Chuang strode briskly on to the court.

He emerged victor in the men's singles; with Li Fu-jung he won the men's doubles; and he and Hu Ke-min were runners-up in the mixed doubles.

The "young tiger" spirit shown by these youngsters amazed the players of all countries. The Swedish coach remarked: "These Chinese are terrific! Even when they're trailing, they keep smashing away. I don't see how anyone is going to beat them."

To Chuang Tse-tung, these championships were a test not only of skill but also of moral fiber.

The Chinese team returned in triumph; they had justified the expectations of their motherland. Steeled in battle,

Chuang and his young companions were gradually developing into determined, seasoned fighters.

FOR OUR COUNTRY'S HONOR

The year 1961 brought a beautiful spring to Peking. Gentle breezes caressed the peach blossoms, and the capital was clothed in soft shades of green. On the walls and in shop windows, there were big striking posters announcing the 26th World Table Tennis Championships. In every street and alley, the coming games were on everyone's lips. Peking and the rest of the country were caught up in a wave of enthusiasm for table tennis.

These were tense and exciting days for the young players. Countless fans visited them. Letters full of hope and good wishes came in from the far-flung border regions, from the offshore islands, from the grasslands, from cities and country-side, piling up like snowflakes in a blizzard. This was Chuang Tse-tung's first appearance in a world championship. He could scarcely control his excitement. Like so many others, he dreamed of becoming world champion. The advice and encouragement of friends, associates, and loved ones rang in his ears, and their faces kept rising before his mind's eye.

He had a time-yellowed newspaper clipping that had come in a letter from an old Chinese living abroad. Some twenty years ago—before *Hsiao* Chuang was born—a newspaper in a capitalist country had satirized a visiting Chinese soccer team in a cartoon portraying a goose egg with the word "China" written on it in huge letters. The old man wrote of his anger and mortification at this insult to his mother-land. He had cut out the cartoon and kept it in his trunk, in anticipation of the day when the Chinese would command respect in the sporting world. Learning that the 26th World Table Tennis Championships were to be held in Peking, he had mailed it back to his motherland, voicing his hope that

China's young players would vindicate the honor of their country.

Similar sentiments inspired people from all walks of life. A PLA* officer returning to Peking on furlough turned up at the players' dormitories on the eve of the games. He bore the good wishes of the men and officers of the Army, and asked if there was any way in which he could be of assistance. The young players thanked him for his concern, but he was insistent. He said:

"Let me tell you what I've learnt from studying Chairman Mao's writings on strategy and tactics. When a fighter goes into battle to fulfill a mission entrusted to him by the Party and the people, nothing is more important to him than the great thinking of Mao Tse-tung. . . ."

To Chuang Tse-tung, this manifestation of class love was an inspiration. He determined to be like the soldier—a fearless fighter who plunged into battle with the courage and vision to win.

On the eve of the finals, the team captain dropped into *Hsiao* Chuang's room to inform him that he was to play in the finals of the team event. At that time, the Japanese held the world title and boasted such famous players as Ichiro Ogimura, known as "The Brains," Nobuya Hoshino, nicknamed "The Savage Lion," and Koji Kimura, who was celebrated for his fantastic strokes. And to top it all, they had brought with them a brand-new technique—the loop drive.

Chuang Tse-tung was well aware that this contest would be very tough, but without hesitation he declared: "I'll play!"

That April night in Peking was serenely beautiful. The stars twinkled softly and moonlight drenched the earth in cascades of silver. *Hsiao* Chuang took his beloved bat from under his pillow and turned it over and over in his hands, like a soldier inspecting his rifle before a battle. On the red-tinted wood

* People's Liberation Army

were engraved four Chinese characters: "All-out attack. Swift smashes." He had carved them with a pin after the leaders of the State Physical Culture and Sports Commission had called on young players to intensify their training, exert their greatest efforts, and play at the top of their form. He had put a lot of painstaking effort into fulfilling those demands. Even in mid-winter, when freezing winds swept the city, he had never once missed out on his daily long-distance running; day after day, drops of perspiration sprinkled the road between the Peking Workers' Gymnasium and the Railway Station. There were deep grooves now on the side of the bat where his fingers rested during play. Stroking the bat, he whispered: "We'll do our best!"

The next night, he was given a difficult assignment. He had to lead off the attack in the men's team finals. His adversary was the Japanese national champion, Nobuya Hoshino, "The Savage Lion." *Hsiao* Chuang won a 2–0 victory, thus scoring the first point for the Chinese team. In the fifth game, playing brilliantly, he defeated Ichiro Ogimura. The Chinese team eventually won a 5–3 victory over the Japanese, who had held the world title for eight years. China thus won the Swaythling Cup for the first time in table tennis history.

How many people clapped until their hands hurt, shouted themselves hoarse, and worked themselves into such a pitch of excitement that sleep evaded them that night! But Chuang Tse-tung was coolly preparing for the next battle. He would meet Japan's Koji Kimura in the men's singles. Kimura, a left-handed player whose uncanny loop drives carried a vicious forward spin, had unexpectedly trounced two of China's best players, Jung Kuo-tuan and Hsu Yin-sheng, in the team-event finals. Foreign correspondents were already declaring that Kimura was the favorite for the singles title.

Chuang Tse-tung, however, had made up his mind to beat Kimura and win the world singles title for China.

On the night of April 11, tension ran high as the battle

began. Chuang Tse-tung, unaccustomed to Kimura's style, lost the first set. Soon after the second set started, he was well behind at 0–7. The fifteen thousand spectators in the gymnasium and the hundreds of thousands huddled around television and radio sets were in an agony of suspense for *Hsiao* Chuang. But he himself faced the table without the least sign of nervousness. Anticipating a strenuous encounter, he had made exhaustive preparations beforehand, mentally as well as tactically. Hsu Yin-sheng, after his defeat by Kimura, had summed up his experience and conveyed his conclusions to *Hsiao* Chuang the previous night. "You must attack before Kimura does," he counseled. *Hsiao* Chuang had been profoundly affected by Hsu Yin-sheng's spirit of placing the collective before everything else. Now, in the second set, he was slowly getting used to Kimura's bizarre shots. He began to apply the method of "attack before Kimura." Forcing the Japanese player onto the defensive, he gave him no chance to use his loop drives, and won two sets in succession. The gymnasium rocked with thunderous applause as Chang Hsieh-lin at the neighboring table eliminated Nobuya Hoshino despite his fantastic chop strokes. His friend's success encouraged Chuang Tse-tung. Snatching up his towel from where it hung on the partition board, he mopped his perspiring face and remarked to the coach: "I'm hitting my stride!"

The game against Kimura went on. Chuang played with increasing fury, slamming the ball with such force and speed that it seemed no more than a blurred streak of light. Kimura very soon succumbed to such an attack. Then, in rapid succession, Chuang Tse-tung defeated Ogimura and his own colleagues, Hsu Yin-sheng and Li Fu-jung, thereby winning the world men's singles title. The name of a Chinese athlete was engraved on the St. Bride's Cup.

EMERALD WAVES AND

A SILVER SEA

[When we think of the Chinese people building their new society, we usually picture a more or less homogeneous race inhabiting the great river valleys and plains of East China.

It is true that most Chinese live in this fertile region; it is also true that the overwhelming majority of them— 94 per cent, to be precise—belong to one main race, known as the Han.

But the other 6 per cent of the population is far from homogeneous. It consists of 50 or 60 "national minorities," widely scattered over China's territory, each with its own customs, styles of dress, language, and religion.

In the past, these non-Han groups—like the non-white people in the United States—were treated as inferiors. The Communists, during their fight for survival during the 1930's, and particularly on the Long March (1934– 35), were helped more than once by them, and the policy of the Party has always been to allow them some autonomy and to respect their culture.

Many of them produce exquisite art works, often superior to anything the Han can manage. In music especially, they are very rich, and some of China's most popular melodies are adapted from minority songs. They contribute in other ways to the national culture: One of the world's most impressive and moving sights is the great square in Peking on the night of October 1—the anniversary of the founding of the People's Republic. On that night, the minorities turn out in full regalia and dance through the crowds under a canopy of exploding fireworks.

But the national minorities are more than a cultural appendage to the new society. Among them, they control no less than 60 per cent of China's area—and much of that land is sparsely populated and strategically crucial frontier territory.

The government cannot afford to lose their allegiance; at the same time, because China has a serious shortage of arable land, it has been official policy to encourage migration of Han people to the outlying areas. This must be done in such a way as not to offend the national minorities.

One important factor that might help to offset animosity is that the Han Chinese bring with them modern techniques in forestry, agriculture, and animal husbandry. This has already produced a thriving economy in deserts and prairies that before had scarcely been used.

Most of the literature that the Chinese read on this subject is made up of stories and poems by minority people, praising the technical miracles that have been wrought in their lands.

A Sinkiang shepherd and his son

Here is a typical example—a poem by a Mongolian about the transformation of the Chao Uda desert in Inner Mongolia. It was published in *Chinese Literature* magazine in 1964.]

Have you been
To the Chao Uda desert?
Have you seen
That green ocean of poplars?
Have you asked the old folk
How they lived in days gone by?
Have you heard from the bird song
What manner of place it is now?

This was a barren land,
Bare as a bald head;
On that arid desert
No flowers took root or bloomed;
Wild winds whipped the plain
Into seas of swirling sand,
And the wrath of the gods
Smudged the clouds with dust.

Now in young woods
Birds build their nests,
Broad green foliage screens the sultry sun
And playful goats crop grass.
New canals interlace
And pour their gurgling water over the soil,
Making the scene
Lovelier than a dream.

What herdsman can lasso
A soaring eagle?
What marksman can bring down
Man's aspirations?
Men have made green waves

Roll over that silver sea,
The desert is now a garden
Where cuckoos sing.

Like shoals of gleaming fish
Frisking in limpid pools,
Goats with curved horns
Career through the poplar shade;
Like thousands of swans taking flight
To wing through blue skies
Are the tireless herdsmen aglow with hope
Whose song lingers in the air.

Good the tang of the damp earth
So soft to tread;
The road strewn with flowers
Is a carpet of colors;

Clouds white as satin
Float unsullied by dust,
And in the hearts of the foresters
Is a vision as great as the sea.

ANCIENT FABLES

[It is a common belief in the West that China's progress has been achieved only by massive regimentation. Many people cannot picture the Chinese as anything but millions of robots parroting Marxist slogans. Such people give the Communists too much credit as molders of public opinion; Party members amount to less than 3 per cent of the population, and they lack the advantages of television, motivational research, opinion polls, and universal literacy that make mass communications in the West so influential.

More importantly, such people underestimate the profundity and resilience of traditional Chinese culture. We have already seen—from stories like "Marriage" and "Stubborn Ox Niu"—that Chinese peasants have an enviable range and richness in the way they speak. Their thinking is highly colored by the language they use, the proverbs and imagery that are part of their cultural heritage.

There are many new things in China—new ideas, a new morality, a new economic and political system. But old China is never far beneath the surface. The resulting blend of ancient and modern gives the Chinese mentality—if we can speak so broadly—a character all its own.

A good way to show how thoroughly traditional this mentality can be is to consider the contemporary Chinese sense of humor. If you ask someone in China to tell you a joke, he will almost certainly *not* come up with something topical. The chances are he will reel off a tale straight from the classical books—one that has been making people laugh for thousands of years.

The brief selection of such jokes included here is taken from a book called *Chinese Fables,* published by the Foreign Languages Press, Peking.]

THREE CHESTNUTS OR FOUR*

A monkey-trainer in the state of Sung was fond of monkeys and kept a great many of them. He was able to understand them and they him. Indeed, he used to save some of his family's food for them. But a time came when there was not much food left at home, and he wanted to cut down the monkeys' rations. He feared, however, that they might not agree to this, and decided to deceive them.

"I'll give you three chestnuts each morning and four each evening," he said. "Will that be enough?"

All the monkeys rose up to express their anger.

"Well, what about four in the morning and three in the evening?" he asked.

Then the monkeys squatted down again, feeling quite satisfied.

SUSPICION †

A man who lost his ax suspected his neighbor's son of stealing it. He watched the way the lad walked—exactly like a thief. He watched the boy's expression—it was that of a thief. He watched the way he talked—just like a thief. In short, all his gestures and actions proclaimed him guilty of theft.

But later he found his ax himself when he went out to

* From the *Lieh Tzu,* a book attributed to Lieh Yü-kou, who lived some time between the seventh and the fifth century B.C.
† Also from the *Lieh Tzu*

dig. And after that, when he saw his neighbor's son, all the lad's gestures and actions looked quite unlike those of a thief.

THE MAN WHO SOLD SPEARS AND SHIELDS *

In the state of Chu lived a man who sold shields and spears.

"My shields are so strong," he boasted, "that nothing can pierce them. My spears are so sharp there is nothing they cannot pierce."

"What if one of your spears strikes one of your shields?" someone asked him.

The man had no answer to that.

BUYING A PAIR OF SHOES †

A man in the state of Cheng decided to buy some new shoes. He measured his feet but left the measure on his seat, and went to the market without it. There he found a shoe-maker.

"Why, I forgot to bring the measurement!" he cried.

He hurried home to fetch it.

By the time he got back to the market, the fair was over; so he could not buy any shoes.

"Why didn't you just try the shoes on?" asked one of his neighbors.

"I trust the ruler more," was his reply.

THE LORD WHO LOVED DRAGONS ‡

Lord Yeh was so fond of dragons that he had them painted

---

* From a book called the *Han Fei Tzu*, written about two centuries B.C. It is interesting to note that to this day the Chinese term for "contradiction" consists of the characters for "spear" and "shield" put together.

† Also from the *Han Fei Tzu*

‡ From the works of Shen Pu-hai, who died in 337 B.C.

and carved all over his house. When the real dragon in heaven heard about this, it flew down and put its head through Lord Yeh's door and its tail through one of his windows. When the lord saw this, he fled, frightened half out of his wits.

This shows that the lord was not really fond of dragons. He liked all that looked like dragons but not the genuine thing.

THE CHICKEN THIEF *

There was a man who used to steal a chicken from his neighbors every day.

"It is wrong to steal," someone told him.

"I'll cut down on it," promised the chicken thief. "I shall steal one chicken a month from now on, and stop altogether next year."

Because he knew he was wrong, he ought to have stopped at once. Why wait another year?

HELPING YOUNG SHOOTS TO GROW †

A man in the state of Sung felt the shoots in his fields were not growing fast enough. So he pulled every one of them up just an inch, then went home quite exhausted.

"I'm tired out today," he told his family. "I've been helping the young shoots to grow."

His son ran out to the fields to have a look, and found all their seedlings dead.

Most people would like to help young shoots grow. Some think nothing can help, and do not even weed their fields; others try to help by pulling, which is worse than useless.

* From the works of Mencius (372–289 B.C.)
† Also from Mencius

CHINA SUCCESSFULLY

EXPLODES ITS FIRST

ATOMIC BOMB

[The next extract quite literally brings us back to the present with a bang. It should not have come as a surprise, of course, when China exploded its first atom bomb on October 16, 1964. It was the logical conclusion of an international situation in which China was expected to sit growing vegetables while other countries deployed nuclear weapons against it.

The Chinese Government statement issued at the time does, however, raise questions in our minds. How, for example, can China, still a poor country, justify the expenditure of the large amounts of money and materials needed for nuclear development? And what of Mao's well-known theory that the atomic bomb is only a "paper tiger"?

The statement deals with these questions. Atomic weapons, it indicates, are the last things China wants. It has been forced to manufacture them for two reasons: to make the United States think twice about attacking her; and to break the monopoly of nuclear weapons held by a handful of white, Western nations.

The "paper tiger" theory, the statement insists, still holds true. Nuclear weapons are indeed very destructive, but in the long run it is people, not weapons, who decide the outcome of a war. Even if the United States (and, one might now add, the Soviet Union) were insane enough to atom bomb China, the Chinese people would not only survive but would go on to win the man-to-man battle on the ground.

This has sometimes been interpreted as a cruel approach, as if Mao were willing to sacrifice half his population. The Chinese are quick to point out that the cruelty lies with those who brandish the weapons, not with those who desperately seek ways to defend themselves.

Whatever the case, China's possession of nuclear weapons will eventually force the big powers to treat it as an equal in disarmament and other discussions. As one quarter of mankind, the Chinese presumably feel entitled to be at the table when issues affecting the fate of humanity are discussed.

In China, when a bomb is exploded, the people pour into the streets to celebrate the occasion. Having never used it in war, they feel no guilt about it. It is seen as a

On-the-job training at the Anshan
Iron and Steel Works, Shanghai

great national asset, a sign that China has caught up with the advanced countries in military technology.

So China has made its entry into the world community. Those who do not like the way it has done it should remember that it feels itself to have been systematically excluded from world bodies like the United Nations for many years, and subjected to a constant threat of nuclear attack.

One thing is certain: The China that is now making the rich and powerful nations sit up and listen is a very different country from the one we saw in the early sections of this book. The "sick man of Asia" has made a dramatic recovery.]

CHINESE GOVERNMENT STATEMENT, OCTOBER 16, 1964

China exploded an atom bomb at 15:00 hours on October 16, 1964, and thereby successfully conducted its first nuclear test. This is a major achievement of the Chinese people in their struggle to increase their national defense capability and to oppose the U.S. imperialist policy of nuclear blackmail and nuclear threats.

Self-defense is the inalienable right of every sovereign state. The safeguarding of world peace is the common task of all peace-loving countries. China cannot remain idle in the face of the ever increasing nuclear threat posed by the United States. China is forced to conduct nuclear tests and to develop nuclear weapons.

The Chinese Government has consistently advocated the complete prohibition and thorough destruction of nuclear weapons. Had this been realized, China need not have developed the nuclear weapon. But this position of ours has met the stubborn resistance of the U.S. imperialists. The Chinese Government pointed out long ago that the treaty on the partial halting of nuclear tests, signed by the United States, Britain, and the Soviet Union in July, 1963, was a big fraud to fool the people of the world. It tried to consolidate the nuclear monopoly held by the three nuclear powers and to bind the peace-loving countries hand and foot. It did not decrease but actually increased the nuclear threat of U.S. imperialism against the people of China and the whole world. The U.S. Government declared undisguisedly even then that the conclusion of such a treaty does not at all mean that the United States would not conduct underground tests or would not use, manufacture, stockpile, export, or proliferate nuclear weapons. The facts of the past year fully prove this point.

During the past year and more, the United States has not stopped manufacturing various nuclear weapons on the basis of the nuclear tests that it had already conducted. Furthermore, seeking ever greater perfection, the United States has during this same period conducted several dozen underground nuclear tests, thereby further perfecting the nuclear weapons it manufactures. In stationing nuclear submarines in Japan, the United States is posing a direct threat to the Japanese people, the Chinese people, and the people of all other Asian countries. The United States is now putting nuclear weapons into the hands of the West German revanchists through the so-called multilateral nuclear force and thereby threatening the security of the German Democratic Republic and the other East European socialist countries. U.S. submarines carrying Polaris missiles with nuclear warheads are prowling the Taiwan Straits, the Tonkin Gulf, the Mediterranean Sea, the Pacific Ocean, the Indian Ocean, and the Atlantic Ocean, threatening peace-loving countries everywhere and all peoples who are fighting against imperialism, colonialism, and neo-colonialism. Under such circumstances, how can it be considered that the U.S. nuclear blackmail and nuclear threat against the people of the world no longer exists, just because of the false impression created by the temporary halting of atmospheric tests by the United States?

The atomic bomb is a paper tiger. This famous saying by

Chairman Mao Tse-tung is known to all. This was our view in the past and this is still our view at present. China is developing nuclear weapons not because we believe in the omnipotence of nuclear weapons or because China plans to use nuclear weapons. The truth is exactly to the contrary. In developing nuclear weapons, China's aim is to break the nuclear monopoly of the nuclear powers and to eliminate nuclear weapons.

The Chinese Government is loyal to Marxism-Leninism and proletarian internationalism. We believe in the people. It is the people who decide the outcome of a war, and not any weapon. The destiny of China is decided by the Chinese people, and the destiny of the world by the peoples of the world, and not by the nuclear weapon. The development of nuclear weapons by China is for defense and for protecting the Chinese people from the danger that the United States will launch a nuclear war.

The Chinese Government hereby solemnly declares that China will never at any time or under any circumstances be the first to use nuclear weapons.

The Chinese people firmly support the struggles for liberation waged by all oppressed nations and people of the world. We are convinced that, by relying on their own struggles and also through mutual aid, the peoples of the world will certainly win victory. The mastering of the nuclear weapon by China is a great encouragement to the revolutionary peoples of the world in their struggles and a great contribution to the cause of defending world peace. On the question of nuclear weapons, China will commit neither the error of adventurism nor the error of capitulationism. The Chinese people can be trusted.

The Chinese Government fully understands the good wishes of peace-loving countries and people for the halting of all nuclear tests. But more and more countries are coming to realize that the more the U.S. imperialists and their partners hold on to their nuclear monopoly, the more is there danger of a nuclear war breaking out. They have it and you don't, and so they are very haughty. But once those who oppose them also have it, they would no longer be so haughty, their policy of nuclear blackmail and nuclear threat would no longer be so effective, and the possibility for a complete prohibition and thorough destruction of nuclear weapons would increase. We sincerely hope that a nuclear war will never occur. We are convinced that, so long as all peace-loving countries and people of the world make common efforts and persist in the struggle, a nuclear war can be prevented.

The Chinese Government hereby formally proposes to the governments of the world that a summit conference of all the countries of the world be convened to discuss the question of the complete prohibition and thorough destruction of nuclear weapons, and that as a first step, the summit conference should reach an agreement to the effect that the nuclear powers and those countries that may soon become nuclear powers undertake not to use nuclear weapons, not to use them either against non-nuclear countries or against each other.

If those countries in possession of huge quantities of nuclear weapons are not even willing to undertake not to use them, how can those countries not yet in possession of them be expected to believe in their sincerity for peace and not to adopt possible and necessary defensive measures?

The Chinese Government will, as always, exert every effort to promote the realization of the noble aim of the complete prohibition and thorough destruction of nuclear weapons through international consultations. Before the advent of such a day, the Chinese Government and people will firmly and unswervingly march along their own road of strengthening their national defenses, defending their motherland, and safeguarding world peace.

We are convinced that nuclear weapons, which are after all created by man, will certainly be eliminated by man.

YUAN-YUAN AND HER FRIEND

[A new society—particularly in a country the size of China—is not built in a year or in a decade. During the 1950's, the Chinese made amazing progress. They ran into big problems; but with good leadership and an immense fund of revolutionary enthusiasm on which to draw, they were able to meet their problems with large-scale and imaginative solutions. We could say that the foundations of a new China were successfully laid during this ten-year period.

It is one thing to lay foundations, and another to ensure what kind of structure will be built on them. Pessimists believe that revolutions run on their own momentum for a time; then—it might be in the next generation—they slow down. "Human nature" reasserts itself, and ideals of unity, commitment, service, and self-sacrifice that had once seemed established as a new morality for a new mankind give way gradually to less heroic, more common human characteristics.

The advancement of this tendency can often be gauged by a study of the education system, for it is in a country's schools and colleges that the revolution is ultimately won or lost.

In the case of China, there can be no question about the quantitative achievements of the Communists in education. They have had great success in expanding the network of schools, so that almost every Chinese child gets at least primary schooling, and his chances of secondary or tertiary education are better than ever before in Chinese history.

Qualitatively, however, there have been serious problems, with noticeable differences of opinion within the Party over the best educational policies for this stage of China's development.

This will be clear in Part III, when we deal with the Cultural Revolution. Here we are more concerned to get a general picture of what Chinese education was like before it came under the scrutiny of the Red Guards.

The extract that follows was published in *Chinese Literature* in 1964. On the surface it is a rather sentimental story about the friendship that developed between two senior high school girls. Reading between the lines, we see that Chinese education at that time was not so different from the Western system. The girls had to pass an entrance examination to get into the school; they were expected to master a wide range of subjects, and the teachers instilled into them a respect for grades. The emphasis was on the academic rather than on the moral or political development of the students.

There are some uniquely Chinese features, too. The girls have criticism and self-criticism sessions as a matter of course, and they spend a few weeks in the year working with peasants on a commune. But these aspects of the system do not offset its predominantly academic orientation. Why, the students still learn the Chinese classics by heart—a method dating back to the time of Confucius!

It should also be stressed that both girls in this story come from privileged families. Yuan-yuan is plainly of middle-class background. She says herself that she was a spoiled child, who never had to lift a finger. She also mentions that the family had a housekeeper. Tao Ching's father, though he "started life with a hoe," had worked his way up to become a high official.

The writer leaves us with the impression that school is fun, that personal relations are more important than social ones, and that education is largely a matter of passing examinations. This might be fine in some countries; but what has happened to the Chinese revolution?

Neither girl makes more than a passing reference to it, and the story could almost be set in the West.]

Who doesn't have a few good friends in the course of a lifetime? Some friendships start in childhood, carefree, innocent, leaving warm memories. But most people don't have real friends until their late teens. It is then that precious friendship binds unfolding lives most closely together.

Li Yuan-yuan met her best friend at the age of sixteen.

That year she passed the entrance examination for senior high school. She was quite stiff-necked when the term began. The junior high kids seemed terribly childish to her, while her own classmates were very impressive. They were all so serious and proper. The teachers didn't lecture so much as discuss the lessons with them as equals. Yuan-yuan immediately turned cautious. She thought a few seconds before she spoke. She did her best to inject more logic into her remarks. And naturally she cut out all skipping and jumping when she walked.

After two days of carefully preserving this new-found dignity, she felt ready to burst. On the third day of class, the permanent seats were to be assigned, and she prayed to herself: "I must get a decent deskmate."

She was given a seat in the rear row near the wall. Then she saw a tall girl walking toward her. Her first impression was of long glossy black braids, a fair complexion, a white shirt with long sleeves, dark blue trousers, black cloth shoes, and a pair of big eyes that looked right at you. "Fine," thought Yuan-yuan. "A bookworm for sure."

The two girls shook hands, smiled, and exchanged a few adolescent courtesies: "So we're at the same desk." "Isn't that nice?" They sat down and busied themselves with their books and papers.

"What's your name?" Yuan-yuan asked.

"Tao Ching."

"Tao Ching? Sounds kind of tense. Anyhow. . . . Are you from the Twelfth Girls' High?"

"No. Fourth. And you?"

"Twentieth. I'm called Li Yuan-yuan. Of course, my name might not sound so good either, but anyhow . . . Tell me, what do you like?"

"You mean in school?"

"Naturally."

"I like math most. What about you?"

"Me? . . . I like to read stories."

"You enjoy the literature class then?"

"Not necessarily," Yuan-yuan retorted airily. She paused. "Are you in the Youth League?"

"Yes. You too?"

"Not yet," Yuan-yuan replied very quickly. "Anyhow . . ."

It was obvious to Tao Ching that "anyhow" was Yuan-yuan's favorite word. While waiting for something to follow the "anyhow," Tao Ching looked her over. Very interesting. A round baby face with a snub nose and small eyes, bobbed hair, the brief shorts of the athlete, bare arms, and bare legs. Yuan-yuan arranged her things in feverish haste, as though someone were trying to catch her.

She hated being asked whether she was a Youth Leaguer (though she could never refrain from asking others), and she didn't like being questioned on what was her favorite subject. The former was the query she was most unwilling to answer; as to the latter, she simply didn't know what to say. Except for gym, in which she was tops, in all her other subjects she maintained a steady 80 average, though it wasn't too difficult for her, if she felt like it, to hit the books a little and pull down a grade of 100. Her interests, of course, were very widespread, but they didn't include textbooks. She preferred more lively things—figure skating, various styles of swimming. She decided whether a film would be good or not according to its title. Stories, she scanned ten lines at a time, and she had all kinds of devices for reading them in class. Yuan-yuan didn't walk, she bounded. She got on and off her bike with flying leaps, and she twisted swiftly through heavy traffic like an eel.

An only child, at home she was her parents' jewel. They let her do what she pleased. In school, anything that involved her became infected with her vitality. She skimmed through her texts, she wrote with reckless abandon, she conversed with her classmates incessantly.

To tell the truth, Yuan-yuan didn't care much for her new deskmate, but since they were sitting together she tried to make the best of it. She herself could never stop talking, and her deskmate's silence upset her.

"Why don't you ever say anything?" she demanded.

Although Tao Ching didn't talk much, she wasn't disturbed by Yuan-yuan's chatter. Whenever Yuan-yuan spoke, she listened quietly, her big eyes fixed upon her, as though Yuan-yuan were revealing her innermost thoughts.

But they often argued. For instance, one day Yuan-yuan snatched up a composition Tao Ching had written, and read it.

"Not bad," she commented. "But it doesn't have enough imagery. Take a look at mine." Yuan-yuan handed over her own composition. "I've written this about my father."

Tao Ching had difficulty deciphering her handwriting. Yuan-yuan grabbed the paper back and read it aloud: " 'His head round, his eyes small and narrow, he is very good-tempered and smiles all the time. He has an awful time if anything falls on the floor. No matter how he tries, he can't pick it up, because he's too fat. His stomach sticks out like a pregnant woman's.' How's that for imagery?"

"It's got imagery, all right," Tao Ching replied thoughtfully. "But the teacher says we should write about actual things."

"Why do we have to suit her tastes? Are we still children?"

"Just because we aren't children any more and can form our own judgments—that's all the more reason we ought to use some discretion."

"What do you mean—discretion?" yelled Yuan-yuan, jumping to her feet. "Who are you saying hasn't any discretion?"

Whenever their arguments reached a crucial point, only Yuan-yuan's voice could be heard. Tao Ching never seemed sufficiently prepared. Her large eyes only blinked in her face. The angrier she became, the less she said. In the end she simply lowered her head and read. Yuan-yuan didn't know how to cope with this unresponsiveness. As a gesture of defiance, she too would take up a book. They would both read in silence.

But ten minutes of this was always more than Yuan-yuan could stand. She would burst out: "Tao Ching, are you still mad at me?"

"No."

"Have I convinced you?"

"No."

"You're the limit!"

Although Yuan-yuan always considered herself the winner, she was increasingly conscious of a hard core hidden within Tao Ching's soft words. She came to the conclusion that her deskmate was not only bookish, she was also stubborn.

Shortly after arriving at this judgment, she found "evidence" to support it. A meeting of the class was scheduled for Saturday afternoon. The previous day Yuan-yuan had bought a ticket for a Saturday matinee, intending to cut the meeting.

At long last, the fourth class of the morning was over. Yuan-yuan bolted down some lunch and pushed her bike out of the parking lot. Mounting with a flying leap, she shot down the street to the intersection, crouching low over the handlebars. The traffic light turned red and she had to stop.

She remained seated on the bike, poised with one foot on the curb. For some reason she felt uneasy. There was a buzzing in her ears, as if someone were calling her name. Turning, she saw Tao Ching, about a hundred yards down the road, running towards her, shouting, "Yuan-yuan! Yuan-yuan!"

Although she prickled all over with irritation, she couldn't very well leave. Scowling, she got off her bike and waited.

"You mustn't go," panted Tao Ching when she caught up. "There's a class meeting this afternoon."

"You know very well I have a ticket for a matinee. Why must you meddle?" Yuan-yuan grumbled to herself. But the sight of Tao Ching perspiring and gasping for breath made her feel rather helpless.

"Anyhow . . . I'm not going." Yuan-yuan tried to push off. But Tao Ching grabbed hold of the bicycle seat.

"What are you doing?" Yuan-yuan's self control slipped a bit. "What right have you to restrict my freedom of action?"

"Why must you go to a play when our class is having a meeting?"

"Because I feel like it," Yuan-yuan retorted hotly. She shoved Tao Ching's hand from the saddle and sped down the street like an arrow.

Tao Ching doggedly pursued her, shouting for dear life: "Yuan-yuan, come back! Just think . . . what if an actress . . . when it was time to go on . . . suddenly decided she felt like . . . going ice skating. . . ."

"What's that?" Yuan-yuan turned her head to ask. "An actress runs off to go skating? What will you think of next?"

A minute later she was out of sight, leaving the exhausted Tao Ching behind.

But, although Tao Ching hadn't dreamed it was possible, at two in the afternoon, just as the meeting was starting, Yuan-yuan returned.

"An ice-skating actress—that's rich!" she said to Tao Ching, as she quietly took her seat.

In the past, none but the most clear-thinking, the most

brilliant classmates had ever been able to make Yuan-yuan change her mind. "Maybe Tao Ching is the kind whose brilliance doesn't show," she thought. She decided to test her. "Tell me," she asked curiously, "that remark about the actress on the ice—how ever did you think that up?"

"Who had time to think?" replied Tao Ching. "You got me so upset I didn't know what I was saying."

Yuan-yuan found this reply unsatisfactory. Obviously, there had been no cleverness or genius involved.

"Forget it," she said to herself. "The girl's a bit crazy. Would she go chasing a bicycle down the street if she weren't?"

The long-awaited physical labor stint they did each term finally rolled around. Yuan-yuan welcomed it as an emancipation.

This time they were going to a farm for a fortnight. To Yuan-yuan, it was the beginning of a grand new era. She had her things packed three days before they were due to depart. She lost all interest in her classes. She was so excited she even slept badly.

At last they arrived at their destination. Their first job was to weed the vegetable gardens. Yuan-yuan and some of her noisier schoolmates thought this was too easy for words. They decided they would eat and sleep together, and announced that they would be the pacemakers.

The first day, they weeded quicker than anybody, singing all the while. The second day they gradually lost the lead, and their singing seemed a bit weak. The third day they still sang, but all semblance of organization had vanished. Some squatted as they worked, some knelt, others half knelt and half sat; they leaned and slouched in every conceivable posture. Yuan-yuan invented a new style—she pulled weeds while crawling along on her stomach.

By the fourth day, the "pacemakers" commanded by Yuan-

yuan simply fell to pieces. The teacher in charge wanted to
send them back to school. Because the girls refused to go,
they were given other jobs—washing dishes, boiling water for
drinking, washing and mending clothes. Yuan-yuan apparently
had little skill in anything except laying out bowls and chop-
sticks at meal times. She was assigned to deliver drinking
water to the gardens. She walked haltingly, as if she were
lame or decrepit.

The autumn sun was still quite hot. After she had traveled
about a *li*, perspiration broke out on the tip of her short nose.
In the vegetable gardens in front of her, she could see only
wide-brimmed hats gleaming white amid the greenery. The
girls here weren't singing, they were working zestfully, seriously. Ordinarily, Yuan-yuan would have considered this a
rather dull way of doing things, but now she could sense an
underlying strength. Thinking of her own performance, she
felt ashamed. The kettle of water in her hands grew heavy.

"Water. Come and get it," she shouted at the edge of the
gardens. Her voice sounded rather piteous.

As the girls crowded round, Yuan-yuan suddenly saw Tao
Ching. Hatless, she was dressed in her usual white tunic and
dark trousers. Her glossy black braids were pinned up in a
knot on the back of her head. Squatting in the garden, she
was concentrating on pulling weeds.

Yuan-yuan filled a bowl with water and brought it to her.
"Here, drink this. Don't your legs ache from squatting so
long?"

Tao Ching raised her head and smiled. "It doesn't bother
me. I'm used to it."

"What do you mean? Do you work in the garden in Peking
every day?"

"Of course not. But every year my dad sends me back to
our old village to work during my summer vacation. For most
of the jobs they give me, I have to squat."

"Your dad? Isn't he some kind of department head?"

"Yes. But he started work carrying a hoe."

"Oh. Anyhow . . ."

Yuan-yuan collected the bowls and limped back with her empty kettle. She thought of her own doting parents. Her mother never even let her fold up her own quilt. No wonder her legs had so little stamina.

She had a bit more respect for Tao Ching when they all returned to school. But she didn't agree with her opinion that home life had such a big influence on a girl. Anyhow, her own environment was quite good. Both of her parents were cadres, so her ideology ought to be pretty good. And that was the main thing.

Besides, there was also this business of initiative. Right. Initiative was still more important. From now on, she would fold her own bedding whether her mother let her or not. If her old housekeeper wouldn't allow her to sweep the floor, she'd insist.

From the day Yuan-yuan started exercising her initiative, she showed a marked change indeed. At home, she washed the dishes, put out the ashes, made the beds, folded the quilts. She wanted to do all the house work. In school, the moment she swung into action the fifty desks and chairs in her classroom were turned legs in the air and scrubbed from bottom to top.

She also borrowed three novels, intending to read them in her spare time. As an educated worker, she couldn't afford to neglect culture, could she? But when she dipped into the first book, she couldn't put it down. She went on reading it surreptitiously in class.

Tao Ching quickly discovered her secret and firmly carried out a policy of confiscation. Yuan-yuan had no choice but to yield. She put off her reading until the private-study period in the afternoon. But that didn't work either. Without a word, Tao Ching took away her beloved *Little Black Horse*. She slipped the book under her and sat on it. With her big eyes on Yuan-yuan, she smiled apologetically.

"Dear Tao Ching, give it back to me."

"Not during private study."

"Give it to me. Just this once."

"Nothing doing."

"Are you going to give me back that book or not?"

"I'm not."

Yuan-yuan was furious. She flung her text down on the desk with a bang. "Stubborn, stiff old stick!"

"Don't talk like that, Yuan-yuan—"

"Oh, so you won't let me speak either? *You* can do whatever you like, but *I* can't say anything. I *will* speak, anyhow, I *will!*"

"I'm not going to quarrel with you, Yuan-yuan. We're not children. Don't be willful. Stop always taking the easiest way out."

Yuan-yuan was enraged by this accusation. "Where do you come off pinning labels on me?" she demanded.

Tao Ching didn't know how to argue. When Yuan-yuan got through ranting, she merely remarked: "I'm going to keep on doing my best for you, no matter what you say."

Youth Leaguers criticized Tao Ching for being too simple and hard in her methods with Yuan-yuan. Other classmates blamed Yuan-yuan for her refusal to accept criticism; they said she wouldn't listen to reason. Someone brought up their quarrel at a class meeting, and both of them were criticized. That seemed to put an end to whatever good feeling remained between them. Yuan-yuan vowed she would ignore Tao Ching. After several rebuffs, Tao Ching vowed to do the same.

Strained relations persisted between them for two whole weeks. Classmates wore their tongues out trying to reconcile them, and when their efforts failed they too became angry. Yuan-yuan asked several of the girls to change seats with her, but they all refused. So she and Tao Ching sat together, not speaking, big eyes staring at small eyes, their relations cold and peculiar.

Then one day, the teacher returned the mid-term algebra

examination papers. Yuan-yuan took one look at the marks and leaped to her feet, desk and chair bumping resoundingly.

"Teacher, your marks—they're not fair."

"Not fair?" The algebra teacher was rather startled.

"Yes. No. Anyhow, that's not what I mean. Anyhow, you don't understand the situation."

"What mark did you get?"

"A hundred."

"Then . . . ?"

"No, no. You weren't unfair to me. To *her*!"

The eyes of the whole class focused on Tao Ching. Her ears red, she drooped her head lower and lower as if she had done something shameful. It so happened that on the day of the examination Yuan-yuan had first gone to have her eyes checked. The doctor had put drops in her eyes to enlarge the pupils, and when she came to class she couldn't see the questions on the blackboard clearly. Tao Ching had copied them down for her and had only then begun her own paper. Naturally, she wasn't as fast as Yuan-yuan. She couldn't finish all the questions, and only got 80.

When Yuan-yuan revealed these facts, the teacher commended both girls, and the whole class stirred with excitement right up to the dismissal bell.

After lunch, Tao Ching asked Yuan-yuan to take a walk with her around the school grounds. She said she wanted to talk to her. They strolled in silence to the vegetable patch. Then Yuan-yuan could contain herself no longer. She spoke first, as if the talk had been her idea.

"We've been friends for quite a while now. But I must say —there's something about you. . . . Anyhow, it's not quite right."

"What do you mean?"

"You're a little too stuck on your own opinions. Anyhow, you're a bit, well, stubborn."

"Certain things, when I do them, I think I ought to do them to the end. Maybe I'm too subjective at times. . . ."

"It doesn't matter. When that happens, I can always remind you."

"Will you, really?"

"Naturally. If you hadn't asked me out for a talk today, I would have asked you. Half the term is gone, but it's only lately that I've begun to understand you."

"But I still don't understand you," said Tao Ching sincerely.

"What do you mean? Is that supposed to be funny?"

"Of course not. You're very intelligent—"

"But a little too sensitive?"

"Right. Do you know what I wanted to talk to you about? It's that I don't agree with the way you acted today."

"I was only explaining. I can't be the cause of a good person being wronged."

"Wronged? I don't see it that way. Do you think it's a virtue to enjoy hearing yourself praised?"

Yuan-yuan hesitated. "I think praising a friend's merits is only right. Anyway, I didn't praise you out of malice."

"But suppose you were me. Wouldn't you feel embarrassed in a situation like that?"

"What was embarrassing about it?" Yuan-yuan retorted. Then, remembering how red Tao Ching's ears had turned, she fell silent.

"Yuan-yuan, will you promise me something?"

"Just ask."

"In the future, will you try to think before you speak?"

"Naturally. Are you trying to say I think less than you?"

"I don't mean that at all. I'm sure you think more."

Yuan-yuan was moved. She recalled what a fuss she had made the last time they quarreled, and said: "I'll never get mad at you again."

"Even in a crisis?"

"Naturally."

Very excited, Yuan-yuan insisted they slap their right hands together three times to wipe off the old scars and begin their friendship anew.

True friendship must be able to stand up in times of trial. Yuan-yuan longed for something terrible to happen. She would go through fire and water for Tao Ching. Since their talk by the vegetable patch, she had indeed given more thought to her actions. All her previous judgments of Tao Ching had been reversed. She saw everything Tao Ching did in a new light. She was determined to be like her, to make stern demands of herself and of her very, very best friend. But, although she looked forward to an ordeal, the days passed quite peaceably.

One Wednesday morning, there was no sign of Tao Ching when the ten-minute preparatory bell for classes sounded. Yuan-yuan couldn't keep to her seat. She stood at the door of the classroom craning her neck. When the one-minute bell rang, she finally went and sat down. The smiling, friendly face of the Chinese language teacher appeared at the classroom door. A girl, very pale, hair slightly disheveled, slipped in before her. It was Tao Ching.

"What am I going to do?" She whispered anxiously to Yuan-yuan as she pulled her books out of her school bag. "I haven't prepared."

Her movements were agitated, her large eyes distressed. Yuan-yuan grew tense at her friend's unusual manner.

"What's the matter?" she whispered hastily. "What in the world is wrong?"

"My mother's sick. I had to take her to the hospital last night."

The starting bell rang and the teacher entered the classroom. An earnest young woman, she had been trying to get the students to memorize passages from the classics, but

A girls' bicycling team

without much success. Now she had decided to experiment with a new method: the day before she had thoroughly explained the text; today she would call on students to recite.

Mounting the lecture platform, she ran her eyes down the list of names in the roll book. After pondering a minute, she raised her head and, with a confident smile, said: "Tao Ching, would you please give us the first passage."

Before the words were out of the teacher's mouth, Yuanyuan raised her hand for permission to speak, but Tao Ching yanked it down. None of the other students noticed this bit of byplay. A ripple ran through the class. Tao Ching was one of their best students. Several of the girls looked at her in smiling anticipation.

Tao Ching rose slowly beside her desk. Although no longer flurried, she seemed to want to say something. But in the end she did not. She gazed at the teacher, then lowered her head.

Only a few seconds passed, but those seconds seemed like

hours. Yuan-yuan's face turned a flaming red at the effort of holding herself in check. She looked as if she were on fire.

"Why don't you recite, Tao Ching?" the teacher asked, surprised.

"I . . . I can't."

Yuan-yuan bounced up. "Anyhow—" Before she got any further, she thudded back down on her seat. Tao Ching had kicked her feet from under her. It was a hard kick; Yuan-yuan gathered that Tao Ching did not want her to intervene.

"What's wrong?" the teacher asked Yuan-yuan. "Why are you jumping around like that?"

"It's nothing," Yuan-yuan replied wrathfully.

The teacher gazed at the girls doubtfully. "All right," she said. "I won't call for recitations today. I hope you'll be better prepared next time." She told Tao Ching to sit down, then turned to her lecture notes.

"You haven't given me any mark," said Tao Ching.

"But you didn't recite a single word—"

"Then give me a zero." Tao Ching's voice was low but steady.

The teacher hesitated, then reluctantly put the mark down in her book. "All right," she said. "Zero."

The girls were shocked. At worst, no one ever got less than forty out of a possible hundred. To give a high school student (and these were senior high school students) a zero was unprecedented. Especially when the student was a girl like Tao Ching, who was always rated "excellent" in both character and grades.

Yuan-yuan could restrain herself no longer. With a moan, she threw herself down on her desk and sobbed loudly.

Finally the teacher got to the bottom of the matter. From then on, the girls all gave serious attention to memorizing their passages from the classics.

Yuan-yuan was quite dissatisfied with Tao Ching. "Maybe I didn't come through in a crisis," she said, "but what kind of a crisis do you call that, anyhow? I wan't going to praise you. I only wanted to explain the facts."

"Explaining again," said Tao Ching. "That's not the way I look at it. Before you explain, you have to consider the situation. Your explanation would have put all the stress on other reasons, as if I wasn't in the least to blame. What would the rest of the girls think? Besides, a little passage like that—I should have learned it long ago."

"Besides, besides. Anyhow, you're always right—and stubborn as a mule."

Yet, for some strange reason, after this Yuan-yuan took a liking to her Chinese language class. She had only to look at a passage to memorize it, so she didn't have to work too hard. Compositions she usually dashed off and handed in without giving them another glance. Her sloppy scrawl had always been a headache to her literature teachers.

Her compositions were rich in associations and astonishingly lively. But her handwriting was simply shocking. This made it very difficult for her teachers to decide on a grade. To Yuan-yuan it was all the same. When she got a 60, she smiled. Anyhow, it was passing, wasn't it?

But now her fondness for Chinese, plus the persistence with which her deskmate memorized her texts, brought out the "mule" in Yuan-yuan too. Biting her lower lip, she struggled stubbornly to write every word neatly. The strain nearly paralyzed her wrist. After handing in her paper, she ran to the teacher every day to ask for her mark.

One day, just before the Chinese language class, she bounded into the room, flung her arms round Tao Ching's neck, and shouted: "A hundred! A hundred! My composition got a hundred!"

Tao Ching, hardly able to breathe with Yuan-yuan squeezing her so tight, gasped: "Actually . . . you could get one . . . every time, if only you—"

"If only I wrote clearly?"

"Can you do it?"

"Naturally. Anyhow, you don't have to worry."

Yuan-yuan decided to become an author. She joined an after-class literary group. By dint of much persuasion, she managed to drag Tao Ching in with her.

But less than two weeks later, when the girls of the class got ready to rehearse a play for the New Year celebration, Yuan-yuan changed her mind and decided to become an actress.

"Anyhow, I'm a very flighty person," she confided to Tao Ching. "I'm probably more suited to acting than to writing."

"That's not the way I look at it," said Tao Ching. "Whatever you're going to be, you have to stick at it."

"Naturally. I can stick at anything if I'm interested. Anyhow, I'm sure I'll be able to act."

The girls were going to put on a few scenes from the Soviet drama *The Young Guard*. Most of the members of the after-class literary group took part. Everyone agreed that Tao Ching should play the role of Alec Kashevoi, the young patriots' leader. Yuan-yuan was picked for Stahovich, also a male role. Delighted, she took the script home and read it. When she discovered that Stahovich was a traitor, she threw the script across the room in a rage. She raised such a fuss that they gave her the part of Tonya, a girl member of the Young Guard.

"Can she play it?" someone asked skeptically. "That's a girl's part."

Yuan-yuan glared. "What do you think I am—a boy?"

At the end of December they had the first big snowfall of the winter. A mysterious air hung over the New Year preparations. The girls went around with secretive smiles, no group letting another know how it was getting on. But the bustling tempo was a sure sign that everything was just about ready.

Yuan-yuan of course was frightfully busy. The carefully drawn New Year's greetings cards for their teachers, the colored lanterns and paper flowers, the games and toys—she had a hand in making them all. She helped, too, in hanging the innumerable colored streamers that decorated the class-room.

As snow fell thickly outside the windows, the whole school was pervaded with joy. Each class thought its room the most attractive. Each student considered herself the happiest of girls. Even Tao Ching, the "bookworm," grew immersed in their play. Muttering her lines as she walked down the street, her air, her gestures became those of Alec. To look the part better, she snipped off her braids.

"I'm supposed to be a boy," she said. "It would never do to have a nest of braids piled on top of my head."

Yuan-yuan went round bemoaning the loss of Tao Ching's glossy black tresses. "Other girls are playing male parts," she said. "You don't see them cutting their hair off. That Tao Ching is plain pig-headed. Why couldn't she have hidden her braids under a hat?"

It happened that for the part of Tonya braids were just what Yuan-yuan needed. Her own hair was a short, unruly mop. With enormous effort, she managed to pin on Tao Ching's braids. Covering her head with a brightly colored kerchief, she was remarkably transformed—into a pretty girl.

A rich variety of entertainment was provided that New Year's Eve. *The Young Guard* was the last number on the program. It wasn't reached until after nine. Although the make-up appeared a bit overdone in the glare of the footlights, the actors took their parts seriously, and the audience was frequently moved to vociferous applause. In Act Three, when Tonya rushed into the secret meeting room, her long braids swinging behind her, she skidded a bit on her high-heeled shoes. This unexpected scare put added emotion into her performance. In a shaking voice, she announced tragically:

"Comrades, the Nazi devils are burying our people alive!"

From backstage came the solemn notes of the *Interna-*

tionale, as if it were being sung in the distance. A hush fell upon the audience.

"Uncle Andrei, Comrade Shulga—the earth is nearly up to their mouths. They'll soon be buried. But, you hear, they're still singing. . . ."

Backstage, the singing mutedly continued.

Alec walked to the footlights, removed his hat, and raised his right fist. The dozen other members of the Young Guard also moved forward and gazed with him into the distance.

"I, Alec, in the presence of my comrades, solemnly swear to mercilessly avenge our burned and ruined towns and villages, avenge the blood our people have shed, avenge our heroic martyrs. Even if I die in the attempt, I shall certainly—"

Tao Ching's voice changed. She was obviously choking back her sobs. The audience of a thousand was absolutely silent. The teachers in the front rows could see that Tao Ching's fist was trembling. Her eyes glittered with tears.

The prompter thought she had forgotten her lines. Crouching behind the sofa, she whispered frantically: "I shall certainly give my life without the slightest hesitation."

But Tao Ching was weeping openly now. Uncontrollable tears streamed down her face. The other performers froze awkwardly.

The hall was tense, still. The seconds ticked by.

Then, to everyone's amazement, Tonya rushed up to Alec, thrust a handkerchief into his hand and advised him hoarsely: "Don't cry, Tao Ching. It's only a play."

Many of the spectators, especially the younger students, had been weeping with Alec. On hearing Tonya's remark, they smiled through their tears and whispered among themselves. The announcer hurried up to the microphone.

"Quiet, please, quiet," she pleaded. "We will do this act again."

The act was indeed re-performed from the start, and very well too. It was something like a long-distance runner who falls midway but gets up and continues the race. An earnest, solemn atmosphere was retained to the very end.

By eleven o'clock, the show was over. Tao Ching remained after everyone had gone, helping Yuan-yuan pack the costumes and props. The girls had not yet removed their make-up, and Yuan-yuan was still wearing Tao Ching's braids. She touched them with her hand. They felt awfully heavy.

"Finished," Yuan-yuan sighed. "Anyhow, we two will never be actresses."

"I don't know about that. There's nothing we can't do if it's really necessary."

"Why did you bawl like that on the stage?"

"I don't know. It seemed so real."

"You're like that about everything. But I've never seen you cry before."

Tao Ching did not reply. The girls continued packing the costumes and props. When they finished, they stacked the boxes in the cupboard. Yuan-yuan hated to leave the colorfully decorated classroom, with its lovely streamers and red lanterns.

"Let's see the year out here," she proposed.

Tao Ching was no less excited. "All right," she agreed. "Shall we stay till dawn?"

"Twelve o'clock will be late enough. Anyhow, it'll be to-morrow by then."

"That's next year."

"Right. 1963," Yuan-yuan chortled. "In a little while we'll be seventeen." *

They looked at the clock on the wall. Eleven-forty.

"Only twenty minutes more," said Tao Ching. "But why hang around here? It'd be more significant outside."

"Why outside?"

* In China, the tradition of birthdays is different. Everyone gets a year older on New Year's Day.

"We could hear the bells ringing in the New Year."

"A great idea!" shouted Yuan-yuan.

When they had put on their overcoats and were starting for the door, Yuan-yuan suddenly remembered something important. From her schoolbag she carefully extracted a paper packet. Hiding it behind her back, she said mysteriously:

"I have another New Year's gift for you, Tao Ching. It's superelegant, supersignificant. Guess what it is."

Yuan-yuan had already given her three other gifts. This was probably the last. Tao Ching guessed: Pictures—wrong. A fountain pen—wrong. A book—also wrong. Tao Ching opened the packet. In it were thirty sheets of Yuan-yuan's penmanship exercises—all written in a small precise hand and each bearing the date of its execution. There was also a note addressed to Tao Ching. Brief and polite, it read:

"I am preparing my application to join the Youth League. Please, please help me.

> Your friend,
> LI YUAN-YUAN"

The words "Please, please" were heavily underscored. Tao Ching was touched. "Thank you, thank you," she kept repeating, not knowing how to express herself. Awkwardly she rummaged through her schoolbag and turned out her pockets, seeking something she could present in return.

"I don't have anything precious to give you," she said apologetically. "Only the braids that took me ten years to grow."

As they left the school, snow was silently falling again. The girls walked hand in hand. Every street and lane was aglow with red lanterns hanging above the doorways. Snowflakes passing within range of their pinkish light were transformed into drifting peach-blossom petals. The girls hugged each other and jumped for joy. Yuan-yuan would never forget this softly red-hued New Year's Eve with Tao Ching in the snowy street. The bells were pealing in the Telegraph Building tower. Someone had set off a string of firecrackers. Now they were popping in another place too, here, there, everywhere.

They said good-bye at the street corner, after wishing each other Happy New Year.

Yuan-yuan romped and slid through the deep snow all the way home. She kept feeling the braids pinned to her hair and adjusting the kerchief over them more securely. Tomorrow, she decided—no, it was already tomorrow—today, she would wear her friend's braids all day.

THE NEW TECHNICIAN

["The New Technician"—a story published in *Chinese Literature* magazine in 1964—is a useful follow-up to "Yuan-yuan and Her Friend." It gives us an excellent idea of the kind of problems students like Yuan-yuan and Tao Ching would have to face when they went out to work in society.

Hsiao-mei, the heroine of "The New Technician," has just graduated from an agricultural college. We accompany her as she goes to take up her first job—as a "tractor technician" in the countryside.

Within a few pages, we realize that she is going to have trouble. She is a city girl. She has no idea of what to expect from the peasants. She goes into the rural areas as one would enter a foreign country.

We cannot help but wonder about the relevance of the training she has received. No doubt she has read all there is to read about tractors and mechanized farming, but she seems to have no idea of how to handle *people.* She is inexcusably rude to the cart driver who takes her to her job, treating him more like a servant than a person. She profoundly mistrusts the tractor drivers when she meets them, finding them surly and impolite. She spends her first afternoon by herself, sulking because she has been sent to such a horrid place, when her old classmates have comfortable jobs in the city. She sits by a stream, going over her mementoes from college days, getting more miserable every minute. Finally, she writes a letter to her girl friend: "I've been sent to work in a tractor team.

It's simply horrible here. I've not even a room to sleep in. And the others are all men with such a rough way of speaking. We've nothing in common. . . ."

The Red Guards would have asked: "What did you expect?" And she tells us quite frankly how she pictured her job: ". . . spotless rooms in new brick buildings, elm saplings flanking the drive, and warm handshakes to greet her as everyone crowded round saying, 'Welcome! Welcome to our new technician!' "

The writer of the story—to give her credit—has dwelt on this side of Hsiao-mei's character, playing up the "greenhorn" or "city slicker" in her, the better to contrast her original awkwardness with the far wiser girl she becomes as the story progresses.

This, however, only strengthens the implicit criticism of the education system. Once Hsiao-mei has been with the peasants for a while, she sees how wrong she was in her initial judgment of them. But the question remains: Why was she not sent from college with respect for the peasants? The answer is that her training, instead of teaching her to identify with the people and to serve them wholeheartedly, has drawn her away from them, made her conscious of her own importance as an educated person, given her to expect better treatment and living conditions. In other words, education has made her a snob.]

Midsummer rain had left the road pitted with potholes. As the cart lumbered along, Hsiao-mei's eyes were drawn irresistibly back to the tractor station set among the poplars. Soon the low red-brick buildings disappeared and only the high garage behind could be seen. Away to one side was the pool near the gasoline dump, brimming and sparkling in the hot sunlight. Geese, steadily flapping their wings among the clumps of sweet flag, seemed like dozens of white-feather fans waving in the water.

"What a lovely spot!" she craned her neck for a last glimpse, and not until the place was lost to sight did she settle back into the shade of the awning. A slip of a girl, in a crisply laundered white blouse open at her sunburned throat, she had a fair complexion, neat regular features, a rather pointed chin and full upper lip. Her braids, carelessly pinned up and tied with a white ribbon so that the tufts pointed to the sky, gave her a headstrong yet ingenuous appearance. Leaning back in the cart, her eyes shining like a child's, she surveyed the crops shimmering under the June sun, the luxuriant bean fields covered with steaming soil.

"That rain was just what we needed," she said to herself.

"What's that?" The carter swiveled round.

"I wasn't talking to you," was her pert reply.

For a second, he eyed her quizzically, then turned his back on her.

Hsiao-mei had recently graduated from the provincial agricultural school. After a few days at home, she had been assigned to a tractor station not far from the county town. She had walked there early that morning from the railway station, only to find everyone but the station chief out farming. He had explained how the tractor station functioned. Before briefing her on her new job, he had paused, sizing her up in a way that made her self-conscious.

Guessing how she felt, he had resumed with a disarming smile. "Do you know what I was wondering? Whether it would be better to keep you here in the station or send you to one of our teams."

"Send me where there's most need," she said promptly, surprised that there should be any doubt on that score.

"You've only just left school and you aren't used to life in the country," he told her frankly. "The work and the living conditions in our tractor teams are pretty rough. I'm not sure whether you could adapt."

"Why ever not?" she demanded indignantly.

The faint smile on his face had reminded her of the

way grown-ups humor a child. "In that case, we'll send you to the tractor team at Eight Li Village," he decided. "Their last technician's been transferred to the provincial capital, so they could use you. I'll come over in a couple of days to see how you're making out."

Hsiao-mei regretted now that she hadn't retorted, "What gives you the idea that I can't take it? I've been to the country every year for practice." It was too bad she hadn't said this, for although she had not yet seen it, she could picture what a new team in a socialist tractor station would be like: spotless rooms in new brick buildings, elm saplings flanking the drive, warm handshakes to greet her as everyone crowded round saying "Welcome! Welcome to our new technician!"

A loud rumbling made her sit up with a start. The cart was passing under a railway bridge over which a long goods train was rolling. She found the thunder of the wheels quite deafening. After splashing through the puddles under the bridge, the cart creaked on to the main road of the town, a quiet avenue overhung by tall old locust trees. It was delightful riding through the shade and she took an immediate fancy to the

Harvest time at Tachai commune

quaint little town, especially to the refreshment stalls with white awnings that stood in the square in front of the railway station. She was parched, and longed for a popsicle.

But the cart had turned into a cobbled street leading to the open country—with its green vegetable plots and piles of dung.

"Where are you going?" she asked in some dismay.

"Where do you think?" The carter turned his head. "Aren't you off to Eight Li Village?"

"How much further is it?"

"Eight *li* from town, of course." He spoke as if she were a moron. "Why else do you suppose they gave it that name?"

The sun was high overhead by the time they reached the lane to Eight Li Village. The newly weeded fields on either side seemed a richer, glossier green, and a faint haze rose from the crops rustling in the breeze. In the furrows of friable black earth, the uprooted weeds lay shriveling in the sun. Hsiao-mei was looking for a brick building, when the cart pulled up in front of an isolated old farmhouse with crumbling mud walls.

"What have you stopped for?" she asked, annoyed by the carter's silence all the way.

"We're there." He dumped her bulging canvas holdall on to the road.

"What's this place?" Hsiao-mei made no move to alight.

"Aren't you looking for the tractor team?" He indicated the farmhouse. "There it is."

"Is that it?"

The carter, stooping to tighten his horse's girth, simply said, "I'll trouble you to pay your fare."

Hsiao-mei stood in the road for some minutes, staring at the grass growing on the small weathered roof. This was not at all her idea of a tractor team's quarters. It was just like any ordinary farmhouse. In the yard at the back, the golden heads of tall sunflowers were drooping in the midday sun. The thick leaves of the squash vines on the ground were dotted with pale yellow flowers, over which bees were buzzing. With a sinking heart, the girl picked up her holdall and walked slowly to the house. The front yard was muddy after the last storm, and in the mud were imprints from three small brown Czech tractors that were parked to one side. Judging by their mud-caked wheels and the mingled odor of gasoline fumes and warm earth, they were only just back from the fields. On the east side of the yard, there was a large wooden shed holding an assorted collection of spare parts. Next to this was a well, and by it stood two men stripped to the waist. The taller of the two, in scarlet shorts, was dousing the other with water from a tin bucket. His companion was bending forward with his hands on his knees as if astride a horse. The cold water streamed off his head and scrawny brown neck and dripped from his lean bronzed back to the ground. As he enjoyed this shower in the open, he swung his arms and shook his tousled black hair with grunts of satisfaction. After some slight hesitation, Hsiao-mei decided to accost them.

"Hey! Where's the tractor team?" she asked, a sharp edge to her voice.

The two men looked up in surprise. They seemed taken aback, either by the apparition of a young girl, or by being caught half-dressed and dripping with water. The tall broad-faced fellow in scarlet shorts cut a comical figure as he blinked and gaped at her, speechless. The other man, his hands still on his knees, raised a thin, dripping face and squinted at her with what seemed disapproval.

"It's here," was his gruff reply.

"Where's Team Leader Wang?" Hsiao-mei had to suppress a smile, he looked so like a drowned rat, the way the water dripped from his hair and face.

"That's me." He stooped lower to wring the water out of his hair. "You looking for me?" he asked stiffly. "I'm Wang Chi-fa."

Displeased by this offhand reception, Hsiao-mei said, "Here's my letter of introduction."

Wang dried his hands on his trousers, and without so much as a glance at the girl bent his head to read the letter, which he then stuffed in his pocket. He squinted at her and his lips moved as if he were eager to say a few words of welcome. But it took him some seconds to get out:

"So you're here. . . ."

Hsiao-mei was quite disgusted. He couldn't even show the normal courtesy; and why should he keep looking at her so severely? Obviously, the people here were a cold lot, with a standoffish team leader.

"Well?" she asked, her lip curling. "Where do you live?"

"What are we standing here for?" The tall fellow picked up her holdall, grinning unceremoniously. "Come on in."

His arms and back still dripping, Team Leader Wang walked with her to the door of the low mud building, where he stepped aside to let her pass.

She entered a large room containing a big kang,* a kettle holding paraffin in one corner, and tools of various descriptions. Leaning back against the quilts on the kang were six bare-armed tractor drivers. A couple were joking together, the rest were reading newspapers or dozing with their shirts over their faces. Hsiao-mei's arrival made them sit up and stare. Wang, coming in just behind her, picked up a dirty crumpled vest from the kang and pulled it over his head, announcing:

"This is our technician from the provincial town."

"My name is Yu Hsiao-mei," she said, perching herself on the edge of the kang, but disconcerted in the presence of these strange young men.

Sensing her constraint, the team leader glanced at the kang, rubbed his neck, and confessed, "Well, this is a bit awkward. . . ."

---

* A platform on which whole families sleep together in the cold winters of North China. Warm air from a fire circulates underneath the kang, and it frequently takes up the larger portion of a room.

"Where did your last technician live?" Hsiao-mei's brows contracted as she glanced at the drivers.

"Ha!" The tall fellow stuck his head through the door. "He was a man, the last one." He grinned at his mates, as if to say, "Where on earth are we going to put her?"

"Where shall I stay then?" They weren't taking her very seriously, she thought resentfully.

"Hmmm, you can't stay here," Wang replied gravely, running both hands over his perspiring head. The dilemma was making him sweat.

"It's easy," cried the tall driver. "She can stay in Eight Li Village, can't she?"

"How far is that?" asked Hsiao-mei curtly.

"Not far. Two *li*. You can manage that." Turning away, as if to say the problem was settled, the team leader said to the tall fellow, "Big Tien, we must start our meeting soon."

"What meeting?" The girl was anxious to change the subject.

"Oh, just a bit of conversation." His spirits rising, Wang squatted down on a low stool and rubbed his bare arms. His glance still struck her as stern, his manner offhand. "We did mean to build some more rooms, but we've been on the go since spring. . . . We had a long spell of drought, not a drop of rain. The last few days, though, it's been raining nonstop, so the weeds and sprouts are shooting up too fast for us to keep pace with them. We've only three tractors and we're all new to the job. In fact, we've had quite a few complaints from the production brigade. . . ."

"Why? Isn't the work up to standard?" She frowned again, her small oval face as serious as if she were inspecting the work in the fields.

"Some of it's been sloppily done." Wang made no bones about it. "This team of ours was only formed this spring, and our drivers have never used cultivators before. We haven't done so well on the job. Today we're using our midday break to talk it over."

When Hsiao-mei had eaten the rice warmed up for her by the old caretaker, she went back into the room. There was no one left on the *kang;* all the men were out at the meeting in the shed. She heard the team leader say gruffly, "Why don't we have another go at the parts that aren't weeded properly? We mustn't let folk get the idea that tractors are no good. That would get the tractor station a bad name. . . ." His voice was lost in a general buzz of comments. It irked Hsiao-mei to be sitting there alone as if she were a guest. At a loose end, since she was unable to join in their meeting, she got soap and towel from her holdall, made a bundle of the clothes that needed washing, and went out to the shed.

"Tell me, is there a river here?" she asked.

"Why go all that way?" Wang showed surprise when he saw what she was carrying. "There's plenty of water in the well."

"Where's the river?" she persisted stubbornly.

"Over that way. Not far." The team leader picked up a stick and, drawing circles on the ground, went on quietly with the discussion. Hsiao-mei looked the men over in turn. Big Tien, skulking behind the rest, caught her eye and grinned. "Ha, our new technician's keen on hygiene," he chuckled. Hsiao-mei was tempted to make a sharp retort but contented herself with glaring wrathfully at him before she moved away.

Sure enough, less than a *li* away, she found a little stream overhung with willows and dappled with the sunlight that fell through their branches. She had never seen a stream so clear in the summer, each pebble at the bottom distinct. The winding banks were in deep green shade, and the thick foliage of the overhanging branches shut out all but a few dancing flecks of sunshine. She sat down on a stone to dabble her feet in the water, her damp hair hanging loosely over her shoulders. She stayed like this for a while, not moving, listening to the songs of birds hidden in the trees and rumpling her hair as she thought over her predicament. How she envied her old classmates! Some were working now in demonstration centers, others in the county bureau of agriculture and forestry. Her best friend, Wang Lin-lin, had been given a job in the dairy farm near their old school. They were all better off than she was here. Quite a few of them could get together in their spare time to relax or have a singing session or air whatever problems were on their mind. She was the only one sent off to a strange tractor team with no other girls in it and a team leader capable of saying "You can't stay here." What a surly, offhand manner he had! And that Big Tien was always passing sarcastic remarks. Every day she'd have to walk two *li* to and from her billet, yet Wang had said, "It's not far. Only two *li*." What sort of treatment was this to give a new technician? She'd have done better to take that cart straight back to the tractor station. Despondently, she shook out her soft hair and started plaiting it.

Just then, in the distance, the rumble of tractors starting up reverberated through the noonday heat. They must be off to cultivate the fields. She had half a mind to hurry back. But the memory of the team leader's dour face, his lack of consideration, and Big Tien's way of talking made her decide to stay where she was. She opened a treasured notebook containing souvenirs of her student life: crumpled petals of pink apple blossom, a scarlet maple leaf, a transparent dragonfly's wing, a group photograph of her class, the good wishes they had inscribed for her when she embarked on her new life, and the blue nylon hair-ribbon Lin-lin had given her. As she eyed these precious reminders of the past, a long sigh escaped her. Opening the book on her knees at a clean white page, she wrote:

"Dear LIN-LIN,

How are you? You know, I've been sent to work in a tractor team. It's simply horrible here, I've not even a room to sleep in. And the others are all men with such a rough way of talking. We've nothing in common. . . ."

It was three in the afternoon before she walked slowly back. The tractors were out, the yard quiet. A few hens had flopped, panting, in the shade of the house, and the air was heavy with the scent of sunbaked grass. To her surprise, Team Leader Wang was working alone in the shed, dismantling an enormous packing case. The long nails in it were so firmly driven in that he was flushed and panting from his exertions. As Hsiao-mei approached, he wiped the sweat from his face with the back of one hand and squinted gravely at her.

"You're back," he said cordially.

Conscious of having stayed away too long, the girl blushed as she asked:

"What's that you've got there?"

Wang swung his ax and split off another plank.

"This is a room for you."

"A room?" She stared at the rough wood, the faded blue characters still on it, and wondered how this could be made into a room. With a giggle, she repeated, "A room for me?"

"That's the idea." He grinned and scratched his head, his eyes on the sturdy boards. "See how thick this wood is? It's the case one of the tractors was packed in. There's enough wood here to fix up a partition for you."

Hsiao-mei tried to look as if she understood, although in fact she had no idea where he intended to erect a partition. She felt mollified, however, by the way the team leader was sweating for her sake and the energy he put into his work. After watching for a few minutes, she went inside. To her annoyance, she found Big Tien standing on the *kang*, hammer in hand, cocking his head to see if the plank he was holding was the right length to reach the low ceiling. A pencil stuck behind one ear gave him the air of a confident carpenter. His remark at midday still rankled, but before she could avoid another encounter he spotted her and called out heartily:

"Hello, there, Comrade Yu! You're back too early."

"What do you mean, too early?" She drew herself up in the doorway, her voice sharp, very much on the defensive.

Leaning towards her confidentially, Big Tien winked and gave her a friendly grin.

"I was hoping you'd be a bit later. Then your room would have been ready. We'd have sprung it on you as a big surprise."

"So that's it." She could not help laughing. Evidently this tall fellow had a sense of humor. His broad ruddy face was kindly, but when he screwed up his small, good-natured eyes, you could see he was something of a tease. Still on her guard, she demanded: "Why didn't you go to the fields?"

"If I'd gone, who'd have made your room?" He went on bluntly. "We didn't see how we could ask our new technician to traipse all that way to the village to sleep every night. A few days of that and maybe you'd have left. So Old Wang said, 'We must find time to knock up a partition.' That's why the two of us stayed behind. Doesn't matter how busy we are, we've got to fix you somewhere to live."

Pursing her lips in embarrassment, she murmured:

"Won't this hold up the work in the fields?"

"We're being as quick as we can." He went on nailing the plank to a rafter.

Having nothing to do, Hsiao-mei went back to the shed, which was bright in the afternoon sun. The team leader, his back to the light, was busily planing a plank laid out on two stools. Fresh shavings scattered the ground. On the clean shining surface he had planed, the ruddy annular rings could now be seen.

"You're quite a carpenter, Team Leader Wang." She watched curiously, whisking her braids over her shoulder, her face much brighter than before.

"Yes?" He smiled, inspecting the board from various angles, without noticing the surprise on her face. In a matter-of-fact voice he explained, "You learn quite a few trades in the army."

"When did you join up?" Hsiao-mei viewed him with new respect.

"I ran away from home at fifteen to be a soldier." He brushed the shavings off the plank and went on with his work as if this were nothing unusual.

Hsiao-mei sat down on a rickety stool. She had always loved the smell of fresh wood shavings. As she picked up a curly handful and sniffed at them, she saw that the team leader's vest was clinging to his back and that sweat was pouring down his lean brown neck. For the first time she noticed a scar beside one of his eyes, the relic of some battle wound perhaps, that accounted for the awkward way his eyelid puckered. So that was why he always seemed to be squinting and had that forbidding expression. At once, ashamed of her own idleness, she dropped the shavings and stood up sheepishly, saying: "You ought to rest, Team Leader Wang."

He straightened up and lit a cigarette, viewing his handiwork through narrowed eyes.

"I'm nearly through," he said.

"It honestly doesn't matter where I live," she declared with sudden vehemence, almost forgetting how wretched this problem had made her.

"That's all right." Wang took a deep drag on his cigarette, then threw it down and stamped it out. He set to planing again. A few minutes later, before Hsiao-mei could sort out what she wanted to say, he carried the planks off into the house.

She found a broom in the corner of the shed and cheerfully swept the shavings into a place where the rain could not get at them. They would come in handy for lighting the kitchen fire.

By now, the partition was finished. Going in again, she found smooth wooden boards reaching up to the smoke-blackened ceiling, screening off a little cubicle for her. They had taken such thought for her comfort that, above the portion of the *kang* partitioned off, more boards formed an alcove reached by a little doorway. Her hands behind her back, she drew a deep breath of appreciation, inhaling the scent of resin and newly planed wood.

"But how lovely!" she exclaimed in delight. "What a sweet little room!"

"Lucky you!" Big Tien pulled a solemn face. "You've got a room to yourself, while the rest of us rough it in our 'doss house.' Well, technician, is our carpentry up to scratch?" He winked as he waited for her answer.

"Not bad at all." She had to suppress a giggle.

Wang, standing barefoot on the *kang*, was apparently oblivious of this exchange as he studied the cubicle.

"Bring me a narrow plank, Big Tien," he said.

"What for?" The tall fellow blinked.

"To fix up a bookshelf on that wall." The team leader reached for his hammer. "A technician isn't a clod like us. She'll want to be reading books."

When the two men had finished their work they went to the fields, while Hsiao-mei, alone in the house, examined her new quarters with great satisfaction and a surge of gratitude. They had hung a clean sheet over her little doorway; it had been sent to the team leader by his wife, but now it was a curtain to ensure the girl's privacy. She unpacked her holdall, hung up her raincoat, and set out her books on agriculture neatly on the shelf. Before long, she would wash an ink bottle, fill it with dandelions, and paste up landscapes cut from a pictorial. That would make her cubicle perfect. When she had finished, she sat down on the *kang* and wished she had accompanied the men to the fields. Time hung heavily on her hands.

She left her room and was promptly struck by the chaos in the "doss house." They had obviously been too busy to clean it up. Below the *kang* lay muddy shoes of every sort and description. The newspaper rack on the one and only table had come apart. The *kang* itself was littered with dirty clothes, crumpled and sweat stained; and the addition of her partition had crowded the quilts on it so close that the men would hardly have room to turn over at night. It was up to her to straighten things out and make the drivers a little more comfortable. First she sprinkled the floor with water, swept away the thick dust, and gave the table a polish. Then she neatly folded the quilts, rolled up the men's grease-stained overalls and dirty clothes and took them all out to the wooden tub by the pump. There she rolled up her sleeves and started washing.

Returning eventually to the house, she threw herself down on the *kang* too exhausted to eat the supper prepared for her. Not troubling to light the lamp, she lay there limply in the darkening room. This was the largest and dirtiest lot of clothes she had ever washed. But in spite of her sore hands and aching wrists she was happy to have done a good deed. When she opened her eyes to look out of the back window, dusk was falling and the rising moon was casting a faint amber light. Where the sun sank slowly behind the clouds, the sky burned red as flame, throwing a crimson glow high on her partition. Still no sound of tractors on the road from the fields—they must have been pushing ahead with their work as long as the daylight lasted. She chuckled at the "big surprise" awaiting the men when they found their "doss house" transformed, and decided that Big Tien was really a friendly fellow who said whatever came into his head and didn't mind bandying words with the team leader. As for Wang, he might squint in a crotchety way, but he had shown genuine comradely concern. He probably just wasn't the talkative sort. Yes, once you got to know them, these were marvelous people.

She pricked up her ears. Still no sound from the fields.

"Why are they staying out so late?" she wondered, and started thinking dreamily of her mother. "She must be missing me, wondering where I am and how I'm getting on. She always wanted me to get a job in town. But why should she worry?"

White shafts of light flashed through the window bars and moved slowly up the partition. The shelf in the corner creaked. Half asleep, she heard the tractors slow down outside. Now the men were shouting to each other in the yard, slapping the dust off their clothes and clumping about in the dining room as they had supper. Drowsily, she realized that they were pleased with their day's work. Big Tien cracked a joke as he took the lid off the rice pan, at which the rest roared with laughter. Then someone with his mouth full asked, "Why isn't Old Wang here?"

"I bet he's gone for hot water. I'll go and see." Big Tien thumped out.

Then the team leader's voice could be heard in the dining room. "Come and wash your feet, boys. There's water in this bucket."

Someone with a flashlight walked into the bedroom and groped about on the *kang*.

"Where's it gone?" he muttered, and flashed his light this way and that. She guessed that he was looking for his clothes, but she was too sleepy to sit up and explain where they were.

"Hey, fellows," he shouted. "Anyone seen my jacket? It's gone."

"Don't worry, it isn't lost," put in the team leader gruffly. "All our dirty clothes are hanging on the line."

"Oh! Who's been washing them for us?"

It was Big Tien's booming voice: "The technician's launched a one-man hygiene movement." Hsiao-mei could imagine his face as he said this. She smiled sleepily to herself. Presently she heard them tiptoe into the bedroom as quietly as they could. One tried so hard not to make any noise that he knocked into the kettle and let out a yelp. It was Big Tien, the clumsy fellow. One by one they groped for their quilts and spread them out, then lay down in silence to sleep. Moonlight streamed through the open window and fell in oblong strips on the floor, while a cricket shrilled in the grass outside. The room was utterly still.

"They're afraid of disturbing me," thought Hsiao-mei contentedly, her heart warming to the drivers. Life here was going to be good. Snuggling up to her pillow, she slept.

When her eyes opened again, the smell of wet grass had pervaded her room and the sky was beginning to glimmer before dawn. The tractor drivers were still sound asleep. Anxious not to disturb them, she slipped out as quietly as they had tiptoed in the night before. The courtyard was still, not a bee on the wing; the grass was pearled with heavy dew, almost as if there had been a shower during the night. Big Tien was squatting by the cultivator outside the shed, and when she approached him she saw that he was wearing a white shirt that she had washed. The short sleeves, not yet dry, clung to his powerful arms. He was scraping off the tufts of grass that had stuck to the cultivator. At the sight of Hsiao-mei, he pretended to be annoyed.

"Hey, technician! You expect us to wear wet clothes?"

"What's that?" She was mystified.

Workers at Tachai commune sacking their grain

"Why didn't you wash these clothes with your own when you went off to the river yesterday?" He flapped his arms in the damp sleeves. "Look what I've got to put up with."

Trying to shrug this off, Hsiao-mei asked:

"Tell me, Big Tien, how much did you hoe yesterday?"

"Not much. Fifty acres."

"That's not bad. And did you make a better job of it?"

"Don't bring that up, technician." For once the big fellow looked upset. "When we went to the fields yesterday afternoon, Old Wang gave me a bawling out."

"He criticized you?" She felt Big Tien deserved it.

"Our team leader doesn't just criticize a fellow," Big Tien answered earnestly. "He demonstrates on the cultivator. He's had no training, mind you, yet he does a cleaner job of it and doesn't damage the crops. That's harder for me to take than being told off. For a qualified driver, that's humiliating. He's strict, Old Wang. He even pulled my hair."

He bent his head forward and she saw an unruly tuft of hair sticking up at the back.

"It was yesterday." He was playing with a piece of straw but his tone was serious. "Young Liu and I had a plot to hoe for the production brigade. Liu drove the tractor and I worked the cultivator, while the team leader followed behind to see how we did. After a couple of turns, he picked up all the sprouts we'd broken off and put them in a pile at the end of the field. 'Let me have a try, Big Tien,' he says. I let him take over. I was sure he could do no better. I walked behind to check, and dammit if he didn't hold those tines as steady as a barber holds a razor. He didn't graze a single plant! Then he got down and called the team over for a talk. I was waiting for the storm to break, but he just fixed his eyes on the top of my head. I thought I must have had something crawling on me, so I stretched my head toward him. He suddenly reached over and yanked out some hairs. 'Hey, team leader!' I yelped. 'Don't scalp me!' He snapped back, 'If we pull out shoots, doesn't that hurt you?' My face fairly burned. Then he said he didn't have my training, but when you're handling a cultivator you have to keep your eyes on the crops, same as if you were hammering a nail. It's no use looking away or thinking about something else. That got me on the raw. I could have kicked myself. If the team leader could do it, so could I. I climbed back on the cultivator and we kept at it till dusk. It can't have been too bad that time, because he didn't pull my hair. We'll be going back soon. He's gone to Eight Li Village to ask the brigade leader to send more fertilizer for the bean fields. Our team leader's one of the best. A bit on the strict side, but that's all to the good. After all, who said we could do sloppy work?" He tossed down the straw and strode off to inspect the spare parts of his cultivator.

Hsiao-mei went back to her room. The drivers were still snoring, while outside soft mist eddied over dew-drenched crops. She opened an agricultural magazine but could not concentrate on it. She was stirred by all Big Tien had told her, by his admiration for the team leader and his exasperation with himself. When she was thrilled by something commonplace yet inspiring, she always longed to share the experience with someone else. She laid her notebook on the window sill, opened it at a fresh page, and knelt on the *kang* to write:

"Dear LIN-LIN,

How are you? You know I've been sent to a tractor team. Well, the people here are wonderful to me. They've squeezed up on their *kang* to partition off a little room for me. Last night I slept as snug as a bird in its nest. As for our team leader . . ."

The roar of a tractor starting up thundered through the fresh morning air. Hsiao-mei jumped up without finishing what she was writing, thrust her notebook under the mattress, and rushed outside.

Old Wang, seated on the tractor, was bending forward to listen to the engine. Without looking at her, he asked gruffly:

"You coming to the fields today?"

Flushing, she squared her shoulders.

"Of course I am."

She jumped on the cultivator, gripped hold of its iron bar, and swayed with the motion of the machine as they rolled toward the fields. Her heart danced as the moist wind blew into her face and ruffled her soft hair. She watched the dark gray clouds turn pale, then brighten, until a red radiance surging up behind them set half the sky ablaze. For the first time in her new life, she greeted the rising sun.

PART THREE

The Cultural Revolution

IN MEMORY OF

NORMAN BETHUNE

[In Part II, we tried to show some of the ways in which China made progress during the 1950's. We suggested reasons for the success of the Chinese people in their efforts to build a new society, and we mentioned certain problems that arose.

The 1960's saw further progress, but they also saw the unsolved problems of the previous decade come to a head in the spectacular movement known as the Cultural Revolution.

It is time now to look at this period. To introduce it, we turn to the third of Mao's "Three Old Favorites"— an article entitled "In Memory of Norman Bethune."

The reader will remember that "The Foolish Old Man" stressed the positive qualities of the Chinese peasants and portrayed them as the basis for China's liberation. "Serve the People" praised the dedication of the rank-and-file Communists and predicted that this spirit of service would build a new China. "In Memory of Norman Bethune," though it was written before the other two articles (1939), anticipates the problems of the 1960's, the problems China would meet as she grew in strength.

Pre-revolutionary China was a simple society in comparison with the vast and complex country that the Communists find themselves trying to run today. In Yenan, the Communists' mountain stronghold in the war against

Japan, government was a fairly straightforward matter: The army consisted of small and relatively self-sufficient guerrilla units; the economy could operate on a shoestring budget; leaders and the people worked closely together in a rather romantic semirural environment. Those were the days when officials wore homespun clothes, and Chairman Mao grew his own tobacco!

Things have changed since then. Now the Communists are responsible for more people than any government has ever been in history. It is not the sheer numbers, however, that complicate matters; it is the changing nature of the society itself, particularly the growing sophistication brought about by the development of technology.

Such a society inevitably tends to breed a class of people with special knowledge and skills. Managers, bureaucrats, Party officials, civil servants, educators, technicians of every kind—these are bound to proliferate. They are also bound to have power.

The growth of this elite became a political issue in the 1960's. President Liu Shao-ch'i and his supporters seem to have felt that China's future progress would depend primarily on her ability to produce enough experts to keep pace with development, and that the society should be geared toward this end. Mao and his followers, while not denying the need for expertise, insisted that moral and political education was more important in the long run than mere technique. Specialists had to be kept conscious of their enormous responsibilities to the masses of the people. If this were not done, said Mao, a class of self-seeking professionals would one day take over, and China would follow the Soviet Union on the downhill road away from people's power.

"In Memory of Norman Bethune" was one of the principal weapons used by the Maoists in this fight. They pointed out that Mao, way back in the 1930's, had been aware of the dangers of specialization. He had singled out Bethune for praise—not just because this Canadian doctor had come and patched up Communist soldiers during the war against Japan but also because he was an *expert*, one of the best surgeons in the world, and yet he had used his skills in the service of semiliterate Chinese peasants, wounded on a battlefield thousands of miles from his home.

Mao wrote this article on hearing of Bethune's death. (He contracted blood poisoning and died at the front in 1939.) It is not two pages long, yet it contains the quintessence of Maoism. Every word became part of the Red Guards' vocabulary: With Mao, they praised internationalism, utter devotion to others, selflessness, responsibility, warmheartedness, constancy, purity, moral integrity; with Mao, they condemned buck-passing, indifference, coldness, apathy, self-centeredness, pride, and vulgarity.

It is somewhat ironic that Norman Bethune should have been made a model of virtue, for he was, according to those who knew him, a rather gruff, short-tempered person—hardly the gentle Franciscan. But this does not worry the Chinese; they are less interested in the true personality of the man than in the kind of morality he represents. He has provided China with an ideal of commitment that is not only international in scope but that also militates against the growth of an uncurbed aristocracy of experts.]

Comrade Norman Bethune, a member of the Communist Party of Canada, was around fifty when he was sent by the Communist parties of Canada and the United States to China; he made light of traveling thousands of miles to help us in our War of Resistance Against Japan. He arrived in Yenan in the spring of last year, went to work in the Wutai Mountains, and to our great sorrow died a martyr at his post. What kind of spirit is this that makes a foreigner selflessly adopt the cause of the Chinese people's liberation as his own?

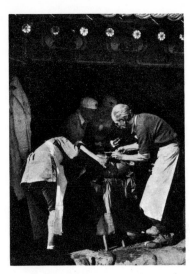

Dr. Bethune at work in an
emergency field hospital

It is the spirit of internationalism, the spirit of communism, from which every Chinese Communist must learn. . . .

Comrade Bethune's spirit, his utter devotion to others without any thought of self, was shown in his great sense of responsibility in his work and his great warmheartedness toward all comrades and the people. Every Communist must learn from him. There are not a few people who are irresponsible in their work, preferring the light and shirking the heavy, passing the burdensome tasks on to others and choosing the easy ones for themselves. At every turn they think of themselves before others. When they make some small contribution, they swell with pride and brag about it for fear that others will not know. They feel no warmth toward comrades and the people but are cold, indifferent, and apathetic. In truth such people are not Communists, or at least cannot be counted as devoted Communists. No one who returned from the front failed to express admiration for Bethune whenever his name was mentioned, and none remained unmoved by his spirit. . . .

Comrade Bethune was a doctor, the art of healing was his profession, and he was constantly perfecting his skill, which stood very high in the Eighth Route Army's medical service. His example is an excellent lesson for those people who wish to change their work the moment they see something different and for those who despise technical work as of no consequence or as promising no future.

Comrade Bethune and I met only once. Afterward he wrote me many letters. But I was busy, and I wrote him only one letter and do not even know if he ever received it. I am deeply grieved over his death. Now we are all commemorating him, which shows how profoundly his spirit inspires everyone. We must all learn the spirit of absolute selflessness from him. With this spirit, everyone can be very useful to the people. A man's ability may be great or small, but if he has this spirit, he is already noble-minded and pure, a man of moral integrity and above vulgar interests, a man who is of value to the people.

LEI FENG

[The Cultural Revolution was a long time brewing. One of the reasons why Mao and his supporters took so long to make their move was that they seem to have lost effective power somewhere around 1960. People in the West, who have been conditioned to think of Mao as an all-powerful dictator, will find this hard to believe. Yet the Cultural Revolution makes no sense unless we assume that the Maoists had to appeal directly to the students precisely because they had little control over the Communist Party apparatus and the government bureaucracy.

How did they lose their power? Briefly, the sequence of events was as follows: In 1959, China was hit by a succession of crop failures. For the next three years, famine was avoided only by strict rationing and massive transportation of grain from surplus areas.

This was a profound shock to the new society. Many Party leaders, looking for somewhere to lay the blame, decided that Mao Tse-tung's policies—especially the Great Leap Forward and the hasty formation of People's Communes—had aggravated the setback caused by natural disasters.

Mao's supporters were then edged out of the leadership, and the Central Committee, under the influence of men like President Liu Shao-ch'i, gave top priority to the national economy. Some of their reforms must have appalled the Maoists: money incentives to encourage factory workers to increase their output; free markets

for produce grown on peasants' private plots; more prestige for experts in every field. These were realistic policies,
based on the assumption that people work harder for
themselves than for others.

The Maoists considered that even if such moves were
economically productive in the short run, they would
prove morally destructive over the long haul. They en-
dangered the whole socialist ethic of sharing, which had
been so painstakingly built up over the years.

They could not, however, do much to oppose them.
Most of the machinery of government—including the
mass media, the trade unions, the youth organizations,
and the school system—were controlled by men loyal to
Liu Shao-ch'i and his group.

The Maoists had two points in their favor: One was
the enormous prestige of Mao, which could be used in
support of their attempt at a comeback; the other was
the army, where Defense Minister Lin Piao, a strong
Maoist, would give them backing.

The way they used these assets was typically Chinese.
Instead of thinking in purely military terms or engaging
in sheer power politics, they began a campaign to publicize Mao's ideas within the army. Out of this movement
came the appearance of a whole series of "culture heroes"
—soldiers, for the most part, whose fame soon spread
from the army into society.

Heroes—particularly those exemplifying moral values—
have always been important in China. In a sense, they
are important in any culture. Every country seems to
have a set of ideal people, whose deeds, usually exaggerated, are written up in school textbooks and newspapers for imitation. They often tell a lot about a nation.
The fluctuating popularity of the Beatles, Steve Mc-
Queen, Martin Luther King, or Che Guevara is a kind
of index to the mood of American society. And the same
goes for China.

The next story is about Lei Feng—probably the most
successful of China's soldier-heroes. After him, there were
others, each one more Maoist than the last. But Lei Feng

Lei Feng—with an old woman and a child

caught on best of all—partly because there were organized campaigns to "Learn from Lei Feng," and partly because the character of the man captured the imagination of the Chinese public.

Lei Feng was a member of the PLA, or People's Liberation Army; yet the qualities that made him famous are hardly those we normally associate with the military. He is portrayed as a paragon of humility, modesty, thrift, patience, diligence, politeness, and generosity. His story reads more like the life of a saint than that of a soldier. In our own military history, we would have to go back to the "chivalrous knights of yore" to find even a rough approximation to Lei Feng.

He comes through in this extract as a rather minor-key hero, bordering on the comical in his boy-scout efforts to help old ladies and children. Under this "good deed for the day" exterior, however, is a profound lack of belligerence. There is hardly a trace, for example, of the warrior heroism that the Japanese still admire so much in their *samurai*.

No one pretends that all Chinese are like Lei Feng, or

even that Lei Feng was half as good as this idealized portrait. The important thing is that a model of selflessness and service became so popular. The Chinese are moving from a society where selfishness was the *rule*—where it was institutionalized in the form of family, clan, and class loyalties—to one where it is castigated as abnormal and wrong. Lei Feng is a symbol of this change. If we are tempted to dismiss him with a smile as "too good to be true" or as "a political maneuver by the Maoists," that does not lessen his relevance for the Chinese.]

AN ADMIRABLE "FOOL"

I want to be of use to our people and our country. If that means being a "fool," I am glad to be a "fool" of this sort. (From *Lei Feng's Diary*)

Lei Feng made a box in which to keep the screws, bits of wire, toothpaste tubes, rags, worn-out gloves, and other scrap that he collected. He called this his "treasure chest."

And that treasure chest was extremely useful.

If a screw was missing from the truck or a part broke down, Lei Feng searched through his treasure chest and made do if possible with something there. Only in case of extreme necessity did he ask the leadership for a replacement. He washed the rags and old gloves and used them as dusters, returning the new dusters that were issued to him. As for the toothpaste tubes and wire, when he had collected a sufficient amount he sold it as scrap and handed in the proceeds to his unit.

When summer uniforms were issued, each man received two uniforms, two shirts, and two pairs of shoes. From 1961 on, however, Lei Feng drew only one uniform, one shirt, and one pair of shoes.

"Why not take two?" asked the officer-in-charge.

"There's still plenty of wear in this uniform I have on, if

"Nothing secret about it. I'm in the PLA." With that, he trundled his barrow up the ramp.

Thwarted yet impressed, the announcer watched him go. "So you won't tell me," she muttered. "Well, I've ways of finding out!"

The enthusiastic race against time put everyone in high spirits. They completed a whole day's work in half the time. Lei Feng, mopping his face with his shirt, could have sung for joy. As he picked up his tunic to go, a crowd suddenly sprang up around him. A cadre in a white shirt stepped forward to grip his hand and said cordially:

"I want to thank you on behalf of all the comrades at this work site."

There was a hearty burst of applause. In considerable embarrassment, Lei Feng replied: "I'm only doing my duty, the same as everyone else."

"You've worked with us all this time and we still don't even know your name," said the cadre in the white shirt. "Please tell us."

"It makes no difference. I must be getting back."

But the crowd would not let him go. A workman, catching him by the arm, pointed at the man in the white shirt and said: "He's one of the heads of this section. So own up!"

Lei Feng was very moved to know that the leading cadres had been working with all the rest.

"I've learned a lesson here today," he said, evading the question. "You all gave everything to the job."

"It's your name we want to know," the announcer insisted, smiling.

He had no choice then but to tell them his name.

A few minutes later the girl could be heard announcing: "We must thank the PLA and learn from Comrade Lei Feng. . . ."

Meanwhile the work site leadership had got the people to write a letter of thanks on red paper. They marched off with it, beating gongs and drums, to escort Lei Feng back to his unit.

This was how Lei Feng, on his own initiative, added brick by brick to the building of socialism by doing one good deed after another for the people. Knowledge of his exemplary conduct was not confined to his own company or to the civilians near their base, but spread all along the northeast railway. People used to say: "When Lei Feng drives his truck a thousand *li*, he does a whole trainload of good deeds."

Toward the end of April, 1961, he was sent off on an assignment to Fushun. The train he took was so crowded that the attendants were rushed off their feet. Lei Feng knew that his duty as a Communist was to serve the people wholeheartedly. He gave up his seat to an old woman who could not find one, and he went off to act as an attendant. First he swept out the carriage, then he polished all the windows and fetched drinking water for the passengers. An old woman said to him with friendly concern: "You're all in a lather from working so hard. Have a rest."

Lei Feng answered: "I'm not tired."

Peking citizens planting street trees

crowds. By asking the way left and right for nearly two hours, they finally found her son. Before the old woman even asked after his health, she told him: "If it weren't for this child here, I'd never have found you."

Both the mother and the son gripped Lei Feng's hands, reluctant to let him go; they saw him a long distance on his way.

Why did Lei Feng make a point of doing people such good turns? He wrote in his diary: "There's a limit to one individual's life, but there's no limit to serving the people. I mean to devote my limited life to unlimited service of the people."

A PAINSTAKING GARDENER

A true revolutionary, to my mind, must be selfless. Everything he does must be of benefit to the people. There is no end to his responsibility. (From *Lei Feng's Diary*)

In his pack, Lei Feng kept his treasured red Young Pioneer's scarf. There were quite a few primary schools near their post, and the Young Pioneers on their way to school would salute the PLA men or call out greetings. Every time he saw these happy youngsters, Lei Feng thought back to his own childhood and to the way in which the Party had helped him to make progress. In his eyes, society as a whole was responsible for teaching children a revolutionary outlook, so that they would be good heirs to the revolutionary cause. He felt he too should do his bit in this respect.

In October, 1960, he was appointed an external instructor to the Young Pioneers of the Chienshe Road and the Penhsi Road Primary Schools in Fushun. These were new demands on his spare time.

He put on a carefully pressed uniform and tied his Young Pioneer's scarf round his neck for his first visit to the Chienshe Road School. When he arrived, he earnestly and modestly asked the instructor to explain to him in detail what he was to do.

"I'm new to this job myself," said this teacher, who had only just graduated from normal school, "so I can't give you any tips."

"Never mind," replied Lei Feng. "This is work entrusted to us by the Party, so we must make a success of it. Let's go and ask some more experienced instructors."

From that day on, he constantly made time to visit both schools and to supervise the children's homework or tell them stories. He was most concerned that the children should study well. One day he found six girls in a study group at the Penhsi Road School cudgeling their brains over a sum. He asked how they were getting on and whether they had any problems.

The girls were very pleased to see him. But, although they exchanged glances, no one liked to admit that the sum had stumped them.

"Don't be shy," said Lei Feng, grasping the situation. "If you don't understand, ask."

As soon as they had explained the problem, he picked up a piece of chalk and showed them how to work the sum out. When he asked if they understood now, five of them chorused "Yes." But one girl hung her head and said nothing. He went on explaining in detail until her faced cleared. Only then did he put down the chalk. He summed this up by saying: "When we don't understand things, we should ask. Otherwise we'll never learn."

He often checked up on the children's homework and gave them extra coaching. A pupil at the Chienshe Road School was not a bad student, but his writing was poor. Lei Feng showed him the best position to sit in to write the characters, and guided his hand while he practiced them stroke by stroke.

He discovered that the discipline in certain classrooms was bad. Some of the children sat hunched up in class playing with little mirrors and knives or reading picture books. He decided to give them special help, and began to tell them stories about the great fighter Chiu Shao-yun in the Korean War, how strictly he had observed army discipline to win victory at the cost of his life. The children listened open mouthed, entranced, without stirring. Many of them expressed their determination to obey the rules, to study hard, and to be Chairman Mao's good children. Those who had previously larked about gradually began to pay better attention in class.

Lei Feng not only reasoned patiently with the children in this way, but he also set them a good example and lost no opportunity to help them forge ahead.

One winter morning in 1960, some of the children saw him collecting manure in the road. Surprised, they asked him: "Instructor Lei, why should a soldier collect manure?"

He smilingly explained to them the need to boost agriculture and grain production. This behavior made a very deep impression on the children, who said: "The Communist Youth League has called on us to grow sunflowers. We'd better start collecting manure, too." Inspired by Lei Feng's example, the Young Pioneers of the Chienshe Road School began collecting fertilizer on Sunday mornings.

Like an indefatigable gardener, Lei Feng lovingly tended these sprigs of the younger generation. He became a good friend of the Young Pioneers, and made a lasting impression on them. The children said, "We must study hard and follow Uncle Lei Feng's example. That way we will become worthy successors to the cause of communism."

AN IMMORTAL FIGHTER

I must always remember these words:
        Treat comrades with the warmth of spring,
        Treat work with the ardor of summer,

> Treat individualism like the autumn wind blowing
> down dead leaves,
> Treat the enemy with the ruthlessness of winter."

> (From *Lei Feng's Diary*)

At 8:00 A.M. on August 15, 1962, a fine rain was falling when Lei Feng and his assistant brought their truck back from a mission. Lei Feng jumped out and asked the assistant to park the truck where he could overhaul it and wash the mud off.

The assistant slid across to the driver's seat and started up. The truck vibrated as the engine roared and churned up mud as it began backing. Lei Feng stood behind, signaling directions: "Left, left! Back, back. . . ."

The puddles of rain on the ground were very slippery. As the truck turned, it skidded into a post in a barbed-wire fence. Lei Feng was absorbed in giving directions and did not see the post, which crashed down on his head. He fell unconscious. . . .

The assistant company commander himself drove at top speed from Fushun to Shenyang, aware that there was not a moment to lose. A first-rate driver, he covered the distance in record time, bringing back the best doctors in Shenyang.

But it was too late to save Lei Feng. The local doctors had done all they could, but he had lost so much blood from his head injuries that he could not hear the assistant company commander calling his name, could not hear the anguished sobs of his assistant, could not hear the weeping of his comrades-in-arms.

Lei Feng gave his life in the execution of his duty.

He lived only twenty-two short years, but his life was a glorious one.

He was born in bitterness, but he grew up in sweetness, and his every action shed radiance in this age of Mao Tsetung!

His whole life was militant. He was the living embodiment of the Communist spirit of loyalty to the motherland, to the people, and to the Party, of utter devotion to others without thought of self. He expressed his philosophy in these words: "I believe we should live so that others may have a better life. . . . I will gladly put up with a few hardships myself if I can thereby help others and do some good deeds." This was his world outlook, his rule of life, his lofty revolutionary ideal.

The people honored him, but he never let it go to his head. He wrote in his diary:

Lei Feng, Lei Feng! Remember this warning: On no account be complacent. Don't ever forget that it was the Party that rescued you from the tiger's mouth, it was the Party that gave you everything. . . . Any little job you can do is no more than your duty. Each trifling achievement or any slight progress you may make should be attributed to the Party. The credit must go to the Party.

Water has its source, a tree its roots. The source and roots of Lei Feng's spirit were Mao Tse-tung's thought and the teaching of the Party. He was keenly aware that "The more we study and the more deeply we delve into Chairman Mao's

No Waste

1   2   3   4

Drawings by Chang Lo-ping

From the Children's Page of *China Reconstructs*

writings, the clearer our ideas will be, the broader our vision, the firmer our stand, and the more farsighted our views." He compared Mao Tse-tung's thought to food, to a soldier's weapon, to the steering wheel of a truck. He studied avidly and put all he learned into practice, making a creative study and application of Chairman Mao's works. This was the basic reason why Lei Feng—an orphan in the old society—developed into a hero and a Communist fighter in the new society.

Lei Feng is immortal. In the words of a poet:

Death, do you boast that you have killed Lei Feng?
In a hundred million hearts he still lives on.

To commemorate Lei Feng, our beloved and honored leader Chairman Mao wrote an inscription, calling on us to "Learn from Comrade Lei Feng!"

IT'S MAN THAT COUNTS

[Another area where the policies of Mao and Liu Shao-ch'i clashed was in agriculture. At one time in the early 1960's, there were even contradictory instructions issuing from the Party leadership as Mao put out a ten-point directive, Liu countered with ten points of his own, then Mao came back with a twenty-three–point program, and so on.

One of the main differences concerned the type of agricultural development that should be stressed. Many successful experiments had been made in increasing production in the rural areas. Which was the right kind to hold up as a model for the country?

Liu's group wanted to publicize the most *efficient* methods, so it chose communes near the cities or in fertile areas, where mechanization and natural advantages had combined to raise dramatically outputs and standards of living.

The Maoists felt that this was misleading. Some communes were in a position to use machinery; others were not. Much of China is hilly country, hardly susceptible to the combine harvester. If the best communes were presented as a model, it would encourage the peasants to expect the state to come up with sophisticated machinery for all—a prospect that is beyond China's reach at present.

So the model the Mao group chose—far from being an affluent commune crawling with tractors—was one small rocky corner of a nondescript mountain commune in Shansi province, inhabited by a mere eighty families and going by the name of the "Tachai production brigade."

Tachai has since become a household word in China. It symbolizes the spirit of Maoism as applied to agriculture. The peasants there had to try and grow grain on steep, hopeless hillsides. By dint of sheer hard work, coupled with ingenuity and persistence, they succeeded in converting the slopes into fertile terraces. The rain—as the next extract describes—washed the terraces out more than once; but they built them up again, each time stronger. And all this was achieved without either heavy machinery or a penny in aid from the state. Even when they were offered relief, they refused it. Self-reliance was their method and their pride.

Many meanings can be read into Tachai brigade. Some are of universal application: that man is capable of almost anything if he has the right spirit; that human beings are more important than machinery or the kind of efficiency that machinery can produce.

Other meanings are more specifically for China. The elevation of a production brigade—average population: one thousand people—to the status of a national model implies that the Maoist view of China's future is that of a highly decentralized, still essentially rural country, where decisions affecting the lives of the people would largely be made at the grass-roots level. There has even been talk of power being lowered further—to the production team, which usually has 100–150 members!

This is an interesting development. When most countries seem to be packing their people into cities, the Maoists decide to do the opposite. No doubt their rationale is in part the threat of invasion. Mao's idea is to build a "guerrilla society," with no targets whose destruction could stop China's functioning and with a people accustomed to making decisions for themselves, who will not have to wait for orders from Peking.]

Torrential rains poured down on Hsiyang County in the Taihang Mountains of Shansi Province. This was the week that Chen Yung-kuei, Communist Party secretary of the Ta-chai production brigade, was attending a meeting of the people's deputies in the county town.

After the meeting, Chen, anxious to get back to his village, tried three times to ford Pine River, but was thwarted each time by the floodwaters roaring down from the mountains. Only when the rain stopped did he finally make it.

A vigorous man of middle height, almost fifty years old, he strode up the mountain path. His way was blocked several times by landslides. The furrows on his brow deepened. If it were like this down here, what would it be like back at the brigade? How were the people? And the livestock? Had the terraced fields and cave homes withstood the storm?

As he neared the village, he was sighted by a young man. The shout of "Yung-kuei is back!" sent Chia Cheng-jang, leader of the Tachai brigade, rushing to meet him. His news was disastrous: 80 per cent of the cave houses in the village had collapsed; most of the crops on the mountain terraces had been damaged and the soil washed away.

Chen Yung-kuei's question was typical: "What about the people?" he asked.

"Nobody killed or injured," answered Chia Cheng-jang.

"Then I think congratulations are in order!"

The rained-out families, crowded with all their belongings into the village clubhouse, could at first see little reason for congratulations. Chen explained: "To have had no one killed in a flood like this is wonderful. As long as we're all still here, we'll come through. We'll make up our losses. If our homes have collapsed, we'll build new ones. If our land has been washed away, we'll build new fields.

"Think what natural disasters did in the old society. All the old people here remember 1920. We had a forty-day drought that year. It was bad, but it wasn't as bad as this storm. Yet my father had to sell my mother, my brother, and my sister, so that he could be sure they'd go on eating! And after that, he hanged himself on a tree beside our ancestral graves. . . .

"This storm has been worse than that drought, because the fields and houses have been damaged, too. But no one would even think of selling his family or hanging himself these days.

"That's because today things are different. We have a lot going for us. Good leadership from the Communist Party and Chairman Mao, for instance. A collective economy. The spirit to overcome setbacks. Remember Wolves' Den Ravine? How we cut all those blocks of stone and built up walls and filled in the earth behind them to make fields?"

His words reminded everyone of the bitter struggle they had waged and won against their environment. Their confidence returned. They felt they could beat this flood.

Chen Yung-kuei's faith in man's ability to triumph over adversity had not come to him easily. It had emerged from a mixture of his own experience and the lessons of revolution. At eight years of age, he had been left to fend for himself as a landlord's hired hand. As a young man, he and his fellow laborers had struggled against landlord oppression. When the Japanese imperialist troops occupied the area, he had passed information to the Communist-led Eighth Route Army that was resisting them. He had been thrown into prison for sheltering members of the Underground. There he had seen a

Terraced fields in Shensi province

fellow prisoner being taken to the execution ground. As he passed, he shouted fearlessly, "Long live the Chinese Communist Party! Long live Chairman Mao!" This man's dauntless revolutionary will left an indelible impression on Chen Yung-kuei.

The area was liberated in 1945, and Chen mobilized the peasants to overthrow the landlords. When the Party called for agriculture to move towards collectivization, he took the lead in organizing a mutual-aid team and later the Tachai farm co-operative, which was subsequently to become a brigade of the People's Commune. Eighteen years of leading the peasants of this impoverished region to transform their barren mountain slopes into terraced fields, increase their grain production, and improve their livelihood had taught him the strength of self-reliance.

The night that Chen Yung-kuei returned, a meeting was called to distribute the homeless among the undamaged buildings, to allocate grain to those whose crops had been ruined, and to discuss ways of saving the crops that remained.

The production team leaders, worn out from seven successive days of rescuing people, animals, and grain from the collapsing caves, had had no time to go to the fields. So the next day Chen went to survey the damage. As he walked about the mountains, every field brought back a memory of a heroic battle against nature. Before the storm, the side of one ravine had looked like a broad staircase of terraces, bordered by banks of rocks as sturdy as city walls. In the plots, bright green maize had stood in flower and there was row upon row of apple trees. But the rushing water had broken the banks and carried away the soil, leaving maize plants hanging forlornly over the edges and huge rocks lying in the mud.

Tachai's cultivated land had been scattered in more than 4,700 tiny plots on 8 mountain ridges. Most of them were on high slopes, where dry weather turned the shoots yellow and rainstorms washed them out. In the spring of 1953—the year the country began its first Five-Year Plan—Chen Yung-kuei proposed a *ten*-year plan for their poor mountain area. One villager objected, saying: "All we have is high mountains and steep gullies. What can we few do to change it, to make it productive?" Chen replied: "It doesn't matter how high the mountains are, or how steep the gullies. They're not living things. It's man that counts. We'll tackle the mountains and ravines one by one. Each one we transform will be one less we have to do. And there'll come a day when we will have changed the face of our land!"

True enough, in ten years, the peasants of Tachai, with their bare hands and without begging a cent from the government, managed to close in 7 ravines with 180 stone dams totaling 12 miles in length. They also joined their helter-skelter sloping plots into 2,900 terraces. As a result, they became an inspiration to the entire country.

Chen Yung-kuei now entered one of these terraces. Though the ground was still muddy, he could stand on it without sinking. Gently, he picked up a stalk of maize. It was bent over near the base, but it was still strongly rooted. He straightened it and heaped up the earth to make it firm. It stayed upright. If all the plants could be raised like this, instead of being left to rot, there was a hope of saving the crop.

Next day, the entire brigade, young and old, turned out to raise the plants. Chen proposed the slogan: "Don't let the storm reduce the grain we sell to the government or the grain we distribute to the members! Work together to get the same yield as last year!" It took them less than a week to straighten all the plants that could be saved, to hoe the ground and apply fertilizer. They also repaired the roads, dredged the ditches, and sowed a new crop of vegetables. Three shock teams were organized: one to rebuild the terraces and prepare them for a crop of winter wheat; the second to cut artemisia and make compost out of it; the third to make bricks, burn lime, repair the houses, and construct new ones.

Meanwhile, the commune management decided to allot Tachai brigade 1,000 *yuan* to restore production, and 100 *yuan*, plus relief supplies, for the families that had suffered the greatest losses. Chen Yung-kuei felt they should not accept the money, but he was not sure the others would feel the same way. During the day, as he dug earth and carried rocks with the work team, and at night before he fell asleep, he turned the matter over in his mind. It was true that Tachai was in great difficulty. But he knew the brigade should consider not only its own interests but also those of the commune, the province, and the whole country. The Party had always called on the people to depend on their own efforts in building up the country.

One morning, he was out at cockcrow. The only movement in the village was the flames from the lime kiln, which cast a red glow over the house walls. Just outside the village he met a stonecutter called Chia Chin-tsai, the first person in Tachai to have joined the Communist Party. As they walked toward the mountains, Chen unburdened his mind to his old comrade.

"I pound rocks all day and my ears are not too sharp," the old stonecutter said, "but I have heard that one of our neighboring brigades has been hit far worse than we. Our country is not rich. Every cent should be spent where it is needed most. If we can walk on our own feet, we'd better not lean on others."

Chen Yung-kuei gave the old man a hearty slap on the back. "Exactly my sentiments!" he cried. "Tachai has been hit, that's true. But the communist spirit of its people will not buckle. We'll leave the easy way to others. This is our problem and we'll solve it ourselves."

To foster the revolutionary courage and self-reliant spirit of the brigade members, he proposed to a general meeting that

a dozen y
and their
light. Ch
the young
a team of
cause of t
could sure
The famo
When t
work. The
were busy
women o
for compo
work crew
pulling ca
problem n
in the fiel
lems that
solved.
By sprir
field stood
achieved a
The sto
ple created
It put gra
their minc
reliance.
As Che
relief cloth
depended
But our sel
will it ever

their motto should be "Three No's"—that is, that Tachai would accept from the government *no* money, *no* supplies, and *no* grain.

A white-haired old man named Li Hsi-ching replied: "Yung-kuei has said what's in the hearts of all of us. Being hit by calamity is one thing; being cowed by it is another. We'll keep battling forward with all our might. Now, I have an idea: Seventy families out of the eighty in this brigade have some savings in the bank. Why don't we turn this unused money into live funds by lending it to the brigade to finance reconstruction? I have 800 *yuan*, for example. I'm prepared to put that up. We're a collective now, a commune. When my neighbor's house falls down, that hurts me as much as if my own fell down. I can't stand the thought of money lying idle while people have no homes to live in."

Moved by Old Li's example, the brigade members got up one after another to pledge funds. The total quickly rose to over 10,000 *yuan*.

During the next two months, they worked tirelessly to dig twenty new houses out of the loess hillsides and line them with blocks of stone. They also built forty more out of bricks. The tiled roofs glowed red in the sunlight—red banners for the heroes of Tachai and their victory over disaster.

The reclamation of the damaged crops was so successful that the yield of 744 *jin* per *mu* was almost up to the level of the previous year. After their own needs were taken care of, they sold 120 tons of grain to the state, thus basically fulfilling their plan.

The storm had broken down a lot of the terracing, but it certainly had not broken the will of the Tachai people. The spirit that enabled them to make good their losses also enabled them to forge ahead and set new records in the year that followed. The Party branch raised a target of 800 *jin* per *mu*—an optimistic yield for such rocky mountain land, the

REJOINING SEVERED FINGERS

[When the Communists took power in China, the vast countryside was to all intents and purposes devoid of medical facilities. There were excellent hospitals in the big cities and towns; but where the people were—in the villages—there was practically nothing. There were good doctors; but they too were in the cities, and their training had made them into upper-class people who thought in terms of a private practice.

During the 1950's, medicine made great strides. Many of the deadliest diseases were either eradicated or brought under control, and public hygiene improved beyond recognition.

But problems remained. Medical services were still not decentralized enough. Peasants could get to a clinic or a hospital if they had to, which was a vast improvement on what was available before. But the facilities China needs —tens of thousands of clinics, traveling medical teams, public health centers, and the like—were held up for lack of trained personnel.

Progress continued to be made in other respects. Instead of simply copying Western techniques, the Chinese modernized their traditional medicine and used it in conjunction with twentieth-century methods. Acupuncture, or curing with needles—the efficacy of which has never been in doubt in China—got a new lease on life, as did the old science of diagnosis (the Chinese believe almost anything can be diagnosed by the pulse). At the same time, the thousands of ancient herbal remedies were analyzed scientifically and retained wherever possible.

There were also breakthroughs in surgery. The next extract describes one of these—the successful rejoining of severed fingers. The problem that the extract barely touches on, however, is that this type of medical work still took place in the cities, while the common and preventable diseases of the peasants received inadequate attention.

This was another cause of friction between Maoists and Liuists before the Cultural Revolution, and one that the Red Guards took up when the campaign broke out. The Maoist policy was for radical change in the training of doctors: Get the medical colleges out of the cities, and put them where the graduates will know a peasant when they see one and have some idea of his needs; and cut the time needed to turn out doctors—by half, if necessary. The peasants need half-trained doctors more than they need big-city hospitals doing fancy operations or research into exotic diseases.

The article that follows—published in 1966 in *China Reconstructs*—is part way between Mao's position and Liu's. It is set in a big Shanghai hospital, and it stresses the expertise with which the surgeons tackle their technical problems. At the same time, it attributes every success to "the creative study and application of Mao Tse-tung's thought"!

It is this mixture that makes the piece seem rather curious to us. The writer does not sound convinced but simply tacks on bits of straight Maoism to an otherwise orthodox medical article.

What is the real importance of Mao's philosophy to the Chinese? Is it that Mao works miracles or gives superhuman powers to anyone who waves the Little Red Book? The Maoists say no; Mao teaches certain principles, and it is up to each reader how much he gets out of his reading. In the case of this doctor, Mao offers two things: one is *intellectual courage*—a scientific attitude to problems, a willingness not only to see things as they are that the fundamental cause of our failure in the operations was not lack of technical skill but lack of a deep feeling for the workers and peasants, lack of the spirit of serving the people completely and wholeheartedly. In other words, we had not grasped the principles in Mao Tse-tung's thinking. In subsequent discussions, we criticized the arrogant bourgeois attitude that considered it a small matter for a worker to lose a finger. And many other bourgeois ideas came under fire. We finally made up our minds that nothing would stop us from successfully rejoining the severed fingers of the working people.

When Mao Tse-tung's thought is put in command, courage, strength, and resourcefulness immediately arise to help one overcome difficulties. With the leadership of the Party and the cooperation of comrades from other departments, we began experiments on animals. We kept lengthening the time between the severance of a limb and the operation to rejoin it. After a lot of practice and some progress in this field, we started to study ways of rejoining fingers.

BREAKING DOWN STEREOTYPED THINKING

We found that if one is to serve the people wholeheartedly, he must first make a conscious choice to devote his whole life and all his energy to the revolution. This is basic. But this revolutionary attitude must be supplemented by ability and skill. One must be completely devoted to revolution and at the same time one must know how to make revolution. One must therefore learn how to break down all kinds of stereotypes and conventions.

We have many stereotypes in our minds—ideas and conventions from "experts," "authorities," and foreign medical literature. Even our successes can become a sort of stereotype and prevent us from going ahead. To go on creating and progressing, we must break down all of these.

Foreign medical literature states that under normal conditions a severed limb cannot be rejoined after six hours of separation from the body. But Chairman Mao teaches us: "In studying a problem, we must shun subjectivity, onesidedness, and superficiality." We decided to ignore this "limit" and go our own way.

In our experiments on dogs, we had found that six hours was not the top limit. With proper preservation, the severed leg of a dog could be rejoined after over twelve hours. We even had a case in our clinical practice in which a worker's arm was successfully rejoined after it had been separated from his body for eighteen hours.

One easily develops a sense of satisfaction from some victory. Our first rejoining of a severed hand was successful, but we had some shortcomings. We believed, for instance, that subsequent swelling of the hand was inevitable. Applying Chairman Mao's ideas, we made repeated experiments, studies, and summaries of our experience. Practice forced us to discard our old belief and to develop new methods. As a result, we were virtually able to eliminate swelling. Our experience has shown us that no matter how correct the experiment or how great the achievement, we must not let success stop us at any point. This is the way to make constant progress.

OVERCOMING THE DIFFICULTIES

In learning to rejoin limbs and fingers after they had been severed for a fairly long time, we ran into many difficulties both with animal experiments and in clinical applications. But Chairman Mao's words—"Be resolute; fear no sacrifice; surmount every obstacle; win victory!"—gave us unlimited strength. The thought that we were serving the people and making revolution gave us the courage to dare to struggle and to dare to win.

MAO TSE-TUNG'S THOUGHT

IN COMMAND OF

OUR BATTLE

[In industry, too, the policies of Mao and Liu contended for predominance. The Maoists rejected the industrial models that had been held up so far. These were mostly the large, efficient, Soviet-style plants, set up in the cities as centers of mass production. Mao seems to have feared such factories—partly because they were vulnerable in case of invasion and partly because he felt that they were *spiritually* debilitating, that the whole notion of commuting to work, putting in eight hours, collecting the paycheck and fringe benefits, paying trade union dues, and so on, was dehumanizing. Work, in the Maoist philosophy, is not a necessary evil, or some sort of punishment for man's sinfulness. Work is struggle—the fight man wages to make life better for himself and his fellows. It is not a way of making a living; it is a form of commitment to the people, and that *is* living.

The Maoist industrial model was Taching oilfield. The very discovery of oil in China was a vindication of Mao's principles, for Western geological surveys in the past had concluded that China would never be self-sufficient in oil. The Chinese refused to accept this judgment, kept looking, and finally found sizable reserves.

The story of Taching's growth is not one of massive state investment, with high incentive pay and good conditions for the workers. It is a story of heroism—of moving heavy equipment into place by hand, before the cranes arrived; of long hours working in subzero temperatures; of danger and sacrifice. It is a story of experiments in social organization, with whole families—instead of just the men—involved in and identifying with the project; with peasants and industrial workers living together and contributing to each other's support.

The next extract—published in the *People's Daily* in 1966—can be understood only in this light. The reader will get nothing out of it if he judges it solely as an exaggerated account of heroism in an emergency. It *is* exaggerated: The fire that threatened the oilfield could have been caused by negligence; some of the workers might have fled in terror. That is not the point of the story; it is not so much an account of what actually happened, as a description of what *ought* to happen in such a situation. It is an appeal to Chinese workers to be courageous when disaster strikes, to be confident that they—the people—are more powerful than the natural and man-made forces that seem for the moment to have dominated them. It is a statement of faith in human beings, an assertion that heroism is not a gift restricted to a few rare men but a quality of man in general—if he will only take seriously what Mao has to say about service and commitment and responsibility to the people.]

STEEL MAY MELT IN FIRE, BUT NOT THE RED HEARTS OF THE OIL WORKERS

At 1:00 A.M. on June 22, 1966, the site of the gas well where the No. 32111 Drilling Team was working seethed with activity. Comrades of the No. 1 and No. 4 squads were carrying out a dangerous pressure test. Their eyes were fixed on the well-head, as great beads of sweat rolled down pulled himself onto his feet. His whole body was enveloped in flames, but still he hurled himself again to open the valve. Right up until the flames took his life, he stood with his arms stretched forth, as if holding out his devoted heart and marching forward forever.

Nineteen-year-old driller Wang Tsu-ming was in charge of No. 2 valve. He stayed on his feet in the raging flames, holding firmly to the handwheel. He sacrificed himself at his post; but he was like the evergreen fir erect on a high mountain.

Such brave warriors as Lo Hua-tai, whose job was to operate the manometer; Wu Chung-chi, in charge of the engine house; Teng Mu-chuan, who had rushed to take over No. 1 valve—these were engulfed in the angry flames as they fought on heroically at their posts to the very end, until they had given their last measure of blood for the Party and the people.

The courageous, self-sacrificing spirit of these martyrs, the spirit of daring to fight, daring to take on anything, daring to risk everything, will inspire each and every one of our revolutionary fighters and live in the hearts of hundreds of millions of people forever!

Comrades of No. 4 squad who rushed to save the well-head were all burned by the fierce flames. Huang Cheng-hou was swept into a ditch by the wave of burning gas. Not far from him was a water-pipe valve, and he dug his hands into the earth and dragged himself over to it. When he took hold of the wheel, his hand became fused to the red hot metal. Despite excruciating pain, he hung onto it and managed to open it.

Jan Shu-jung, thrown from the sea of fire by a wave of gas, remembered that his class brother Wu Chung-chi was still in the engine house and twice rushed in search of him in the raging fire. He was seriously injured but covered himself in glory.

Deputy Commander and Chief Engineer Chang Chungmin, a member of the mining area's Communist Party committee, who had been working on the site, had all his hair burned off, his face and chest burned, and both hands burned nearly to the bone. But he forgot about this excruciating pain in his effort to find the source of the fire. At the critical moment between life and death, a Communist can only advance, not retreat. He staggered and stumbled into the flames. Comrades from behind rushed to carry him out. But this hero shouted: "Don't bother with me! Shut No. 3 valve, quick!"

FLAMES WERE COMBAT ORDERS

No. 3 valve was right in the center of the sea of fire. With this valve shut, the source of the gas could be cut off and the fire put out.

The explosion had awakened all the comrades in the living quarters. Grabbing padded quilts and coats, gunny sacks and anything that could possibly extinguish fire, they ran to the well site like tigers rushing at their prey.

The waves of gas roared and the spurting flames rocketed as these heroes rushed in to do battle with the inferno. People went where the danger was greatest, where the situation

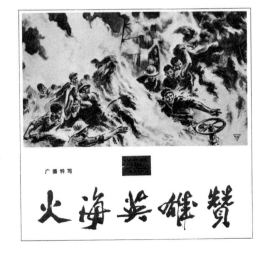

A painting on a record cover, showing a widely publicized feat of the Taching oilfield workers

广播特写

火海英雄赞

League member, grabbed a wet quilt and rushed to the burning derrick. He threw it over the well-head, but it was immediately burnt. He tried with another and it was also consumed.

His mind was clear: If the well-head exploded, the drilling equipment in the well, weighing many tons, would be blown sky high and the entire gas field would be destroyed. More lives would be lost among the hundreds of class brothers trying to put the fire out.

An orphan in the old society, Wang Yu-fa told himself: "You are the son of a hired farm laborer. You were brought up by Chairman Mao. You can give up your life, but you must not lose your revolutionary soul!"

The blood pounding in his veins, he picked up another quilt and stumbled into the flames. The quilt was sodden and heavy, and it slipped as he lifted it to cover the well-head. With all his strength, he forced it up again, standing on tiptoes to reach his objective. It slipped again, bringing him down with it.

At that moment, his ears rang with Chairman Mao's injunction to be "determined to vanquish all enemies and never to yield." He jumped up, wrapped the quilt around his own body, and threw himself on the burning well-head, shouting: "Go ahead and burn! Go ahead and burn!" He lost consciousness, but he had won his fight.

In all, the life-and-death struggle lasted only thirty minutes. The big fire was put out because the oil workers were heroes armed with Mao Tse-tung's invincible thought, men who were prepared to give their lives to protect vital state property. These men have made an imperishable contribution to the cause of the Party and the people!

PEKING STUDENTS WRITE TO PARTY CENTRAL COMMITTEE AND CHAIRMAN MAO STRONGLY URGING ABOLITION OF OLD COLLEGE ENTRANCE EXAMINATION SYSTEM

[Tension between the two conflicting lines in the Communist Party built up to a peak in early 1966. The Maoists were hampered by their lack of access to the mass media and by the loyalty of the Party hierarchy to Liu Shao-ch'i. Liu controlled Peking, largely through the mayor of the city, P'eng Chen. The only place the Maoists could find an opening was in Shanghai, where they managed to publish articles attacking some top Party men in the capital.

This was sufficient to spark a movement in Peking University and certain other colleges. A handful of radical students began putting up wall-newspapers criticizing the university authorities, who then clamped down hard on them. The Maoists succeeded in publishing one of these posters. The news that students in Peking had been repressed spread through the country, and feeling against the Peking Party authorities ran high. In a surprise move at the beginning of June, 1966, the Central Committee dismissed Mayor P'eng—probably as a sop to the growing student movement. This only whetted the students' appetite, however, and posters against the authorities began to appear on the walls of schools and colleges in many story "Yuan-yuan and her Friend." Gone are the days when teenagers could float through school, intent on getting themselves a "good" education. This Red Guard generation is politically alive, fighting for change, resisting that social hardening of the arteries called "bureaucratism." Students like this all over China pushed the repressive and unresponsive power structure, and had the intense pleasure of seeing large chunks of it fall down. This must have given them a sense of participation and power such as few students in the West have ever experienced.]

Dear CENTRAL COMMITTEE OF THE CHINESE COMMUNIST PARTY,
Dear CHAIRMAN MAO,

We are senior graduating students of the Peking No. 1 Girls' Middle School. With powerful revolutionary sentiments filling our hearts, we are writing to you to express our determination to destroy the old educational system in its entirety.

We feel increasingly that we young people are a key generation. The history of the proletarian revolution has turned Peking into the center of the world revolution, and our respected and beloved Chairman Mao has become the great standard-bearer of the world revolution. The Chinese people have become its main force; China has become its red base. We must therefore defend the red political power won at the cost of the blood and the lives of countless revolutionary martyrs and predecessors. We must inherit this spirit and carry the revolution resolutely through to the end. We must shoulder the heavy task of wiping out imperialism, revisionism, and the reactionaries of various countries, and carry the world revolution through to the end. We must take on Mao Tse-tung's invincible thought, and see that it gets to the next generation, which is truly a crucial one!

Dear Central Committee of the Party and dear Chairman Mao, you have placed boundless hope in us. You have said: "The world is yours as well as ours, but in the last analysis it is yours. You young people, full of vigor and vitality, are in the bloom of life, like the sun at eight or nine in the morning. Our hopes are placed in you. . . . The world belongs to you. China's future belongs to you."

As students who will soon graduate from senior-middle school, the responsibility falls first of all on our shoulders to smash the old college entrance examination system. We hold that the existing system is a continuation of the old feudal examinations dating back thousands of years. It is a most backward and reactionary educational system. It runs counter to the educational policy laid down by Chairman Mao, who says that education must serve the working class and be integrated with productive labor. "Our educational policy must enable everyone who receives an education to develop morally, intellectually, and physically, and to become a well-educated worker imbued with a socialist consciousness."

The present educational system, far from corresponding to this directive of Chairman Mao, actually aggravates and prolongs the differences between manual and mental labor, between workers and peasants, and between town and country.

Specifically, we make the following charges against it:

1. Many young people are led not to study for the revolution but to immerse themselves in books for the university entrance examination and to pay no heed to politics. Quite a number of students have been indoctrinated with such gravely reactionary ideas of the exploiting classes as "book learning above all else," "achieving fame," "becoming experts," "making one's own way," and so on. The present system encourages these ideas.

2. It makes many schools concentrate on trying to get a high percentage of their students into college, aiming to become thereby "special schools," which enroll "outstanding

students." Such schools have opened their gates wide to book-worms and apolitical students but have kept out large numbers of bright children from the families of workers, peasants, and revolutionary leaders.

3. It seriously hampers students from developing morally, intellectually, and physically—particularly morally. It fundamentally ignores the ideological revolutionization of the youth.

Therefore, this system of admission to higher schools serves a capitalist restoration; it helps to cultivate new bourgeois elements and revisionists. No wonder the U.S. imperialists gleefully place their hopes of "peaceful evolution" on China's "bureaucrats in the field of technology" and "experts in the field of ideology."

Respected and beloved Chairman Mao, you have repeatedly taught us that we should "support whatever the enemy opposes and oppose whatever the enemy supports." As the enemy applauds the old system so desperately, can we allow it to continue to exist? No! Not for a single day! We must join with the workers, peasants, and soldiers in smashing it thoroughly.

In concrete terms, we suggest that:

1. Beginning this year, we abolish the old system of enrolling students for higher schools.

2. Graduates from senior-middle schools should go straight into the midst of the workers, peasants, and soldiers, and integrate themselves with the masses.

We believe that young people of seventeen or eighteen should, during their formative years, be tempered and nurtured in the storm of great revolutionary movements. They should first get "ideological diplomas" from the working class and from the poor and lower-middle peasants. The Party will select the best from among the fine sons and daughters of the proletariat—young people who truly serve the masses —and send them on to higher schools. We disagree that one should go among the masses only *after* graduation from college, for at that time one's world outlook will already have been formed and remolding will be difficult. Some people, once they have acquired "knowledge," think they have the "capital" to bargain with the Party and the people.

3. If a number of students must be admitted to institutions of higher learning this year, we request the Party to select them directly from among the graduates of the senior-middle schools. Everything we have belongs to the Party and the people. We have no right whatever to bargain. We are determined to go where we are asked by the Party and to take root there, germinate, blossom, and bear fruit.

We are young people armed with Mao Tse-tung's thought. We have been imbued with a revolutionary consciousness. The old entrance examination system can only repress our demand for revolution. If we smash it, we will be able to study more consciously for the revolution and also to save a great deal of manpower and material resources for the socialist construction of our country.

Of course, we know that to smash the present system thoroughly will take time and patience. It will entail the heightening of the people's political consciousness. But our proletarian revolution will not let it wait. If a change is unfeasible at the moment, then we ask that it be done experimentally here in Peking. If this is impracticable for the whole city, let it be done in our class only. We have learned in the process of the Cultural Revolution that we must be stanch, dependable successors to the proletarian revolution, that we can never allow Mao Tse-tung's thought to be lost in our generation, that we must not let the proletarian revolution of China and of the world die out in our generation. We know the Cultural Revolution is a great movement that touches people to their souls, a brand-new phenomenon in human history. We know we are treading an untrodden road. But we are the youth of Mao Tse-tung's era. We are the revolutionary vanguard of the world's youth. We must dare to think, to speak, to act, to break through, to make revolution. We know we are on a new road, the road that leads to Communism. We will meet "tigers" on this road, but we will face them unafraid. We look on the obstacles put up by old-fashioned ways of thinking, by our families, by public opinion, as nothing. We shall overpower the ill winds and the forces of evil! All we need is the dauntless spirit of a revolutionary, who "knows there are tigers on the mountain, but insists on taking the road."

Dear Central Committee of the Party, dear Chairman Mao, rest assured. We have the all-powerful weapon of Mao Tse-tung's thought. With that weapon, we shall fear nothing, neither heaven nor earth, nor monsters of any kind. With that weapon, we shall follow the road to the end. Please rest assured, Chairman Mao, we are standing by, waiting for your instructions.

Dear Central Committee of the Party, dear Chairman Mao, please rest assured. Our generation will persist in revolution, in thorough revolution. We will take over the great red banner of Mao Tse-tung's thought and hand it on from generation to generation.

If this letter is approved by the Party Central Committee and Chairman Mao, we hope it can be sent to all senior-middle school graduates and to the teachers and students of all Peking schools.

Long live our dearest and most respected leader, Chairman Mao!

THE FOURTH CLASS OF THE SENIOR THIRD GRADE OF PEKING NO. 1 GIRLS' MIDDLE SCHOOL

June 6, 1966

RED GUARDS

ON A LONG MARCH

[When the Red Guard movement began, the students who responded most actively to Mao's appeal, those who were most outspoken in their criticism of the administration, were subject to repression. It was not hard for college authorities, playing on the loyalty that most students felt toward the Party, to suggest that the activities of the radicals were bordering on "anticommunism" or "anarchism." The moderates would then turn against the young rebels and make it hard for them to go on speaking out.

For many of the Maoist students, the only way to escape this was to move out physically—to leave the campus and the city and set off for Peking to "see Chairman Mao." From small, spontaneous beginnings, this became quite a movement. During the latter half of 1966, 11 million Red Guards poured into Peking. Mao received them—a million at a time—in the square in the center of the city. The trip to the capital had a big effect on these students, putting them in touch with like-minded groups, showing them they were far from alone in their opinions, teaching them in depth about the political situation that had led to the Cultural Revolution.

The first wave of Red Guards to go to Peking went by train, which put the overworked transport system out of joint. Then the idea of going on foot was introduced, and soon there were groups of students tramping the highways and byways of China. They went in mixed teams usually—boys and girls together—and their average size was a dozen or so. Some of the journeys took months, during which the students had a unique chance to familiarize themselves with the life of the peasants in the countryside. Most college students—to have got into higher education—must have had their noses in books for much of their youth. Few would ever have had to fend for themselves in the rural areas. This might be why so many came back saying they had learnt more in a short time on the road than years in a classroom could ever have taught them.

The next piece—from a 1967 issue of *Chinese Literature*—describes the first such "Miniature Long March." It catches the spirit of Red Guard groups in general—the irrepressible enthusiasm, the mixture of conceit and humility, the devotion to Mao. We get the feeling that the youngsters are acting out a role; and in fact they were consciously reliving the original Long March of the Red Army in 1934, the test of the stamina and spirit of Chinese Communism, the touchstone of whether it deserved to come to power.

But, as they saw themselves, they were not only re-enacting the past. They were taking part in a very real battle in the present: the struggle for power in their own schools and colleges, the campaign against bad leadership all through the country, the bid to continue the revolution through the young generation.

The Long March students, on their return from Peking, provided much of the drive in their local movements. They were there when the students went into the factories to make alliances with workers; they were there when a worker-student coalition—under the banner of "Rebellion Is Justified!"—took over newspapers, brought down department heads, and snatched effective power in many big cities.

It is generally thought in the West that the Cultural Revolution was a failure. Certainly, there were setbacks

later; factional fighting broke out between Red Guard
groups, and the army was brought in to keep the peace;
the Party bureaucracy clung to its power, and was allowed
to retain a share in the final compromise. Although Liu
Shao-ch'i's policies were eventually discredited, the movement as a whole was still something less than total victory for the Maoists.

Yet a movement that produced students like the Peking
girls of the last extract or the Long Marchers of this one
—multiplied a million times throughout the length and
breadth of China—can hardly be written off as a failure.
The kind of spirit and the level of awareness these young
people developed during the Cultural Revolution could
well be the real Maoist victory.]

THIS VERY DAY IN ONE STEP WE SHALL PASS ITS SUMMIT

On August 18, 1966, Chairman Mao celebrated the great
Cultural Revolution by receiving a million revolutionaries
in Peking. Quick as a spring breeze, the news spread to
Talien. In the Marine Transport Academy, the teachers and
students were delighted.

Someone said: "Now that students are traveling around

Red Guard posters on a wall in Canton

the country, exchanging the experiences they have had in the Cultural Revolution, we should organize something. How about a miniature Long March?"

"You mean, walk to Peking?"

"Right. We've all got legs."

This bold proposal electrified the whole school. Most of the students supported it. A few had reservations and opposed it. Some said: "It's only looking for trouble." Others thought it a good idea but doubted whether they would last the distance.

Revolutionary determination and strong militancy are indispensable in the great proletarian Cultural Revolution. A march to Peking would be a fine way to develop these qualities. What was there to be afraid of? What could possibly stop them? A group of fifth-year students—all Red Guards—decided to "look for trouble." They would leave their well-lit classrooms, their comfortable quarters; they would forego modern transport facilities and temper themselves in the great crucible of society; they would go to the workers and peasants and steel themselves into proletarian revolutionaries.

The next day, as they were tying their packs and making final arrangements, one of the school heads tried to dissuade them from going. It was too far, he protested, it wouldn't be safe. . . . The young people saw he meant well, but refused to change their minds.

Just at that time, word arrived that train services had been arranged for all those who wished to go to Peking. The Marine Transport Academy students were to be in the first batch. A number of them immediately packed their bags and hurried off to the station.

But the Red Guard marchers were not the least shaken in their determination. They stood in the courtyard of the Academy's Party Committee, raised clenched fists, and vowed: "We are going to Peking seeking revolutionary truth and experience. On the way, we shall study and spread Chairman

Mao's thought. We will not take trains; we will not take buses. We will travel the whole way on our own two feet."

Many revolutionary students, moved by their spirit, gave them encouragement: "Your idea is bold and creative. You must carry it through. . . . If you study Chairman Mao's works and hold high the red banner of his thought, you're sure to make it. . . . If you run into any trouble on the road, send us a telegram. We'll back you to the hilt." Some loaned them packs and blankets; some told of their own experiences on marches.

The night before they were to set out, they were too excited to sleep. It was August 24. With fingers more accustomed to holding fountain pens, they embroidered the following words on the banner they were going to take on the march:

TALIEN-PEKING
LONG MARCH RED GUARDS
TALIEN MARINE TRANSPORT ACADEMY

At sunrise, the fifteen students, opening their little red books of *Quotations from Chairman Mao Tse-tung*, read in chorus: "Be resolute; fear no sacrifice; surmount every obstacle; win victory." To the applause of their teachers and fellow students, they set out toward the sun, toward Peking, toward Chairman Mao. Their banner led the way, and they were all in high spirits. Each had his book of *Quotations* in his pocket.

> Do not say that the strong pass is guarded with iron;
> This very day in one step we shall pass its summit.

It was over 700 miles from Talien to Peking, but it was a bright, socialist road, illuminated by Chairman Mao Tse-tung's thought. Thirty years before, the Red Army, on tireless feet, had covered over 7,000 miles to reach Yenan, then China's revolutionary center. Now, Red Guards of Mao Tse-tung's era were following the road that the revolutionary martyrs had paved with their blood. They were marching toward the center of the great proletarian Cultural Revolution—Peking.

CHAIRMAN MAO'S HEART IS WITH THE MASSES

In a hurry to get to Peking, the Red Guard marchers did 27 miles the first day, reaching the city of Chinchou. When people heard they were heading for the capital to see Chairman Mao, they came out to welcome them with drums and cymbals.

The next day, the fifteen students, united as one, shouldered their packs and continued on the way to their goal.

August is the rainy season on the Liaotung Peninsula. Rain fell almost all the time. No sooner had the marchers' clothes dried out than they were soaked again. The air was

A Red Guard in Peking, January, 1967

(photo: Roger Whittaker)

Bedroll and spare shoes
packed for the
"Long March"

(photo: Roger Whittaker)

heavy and oppressive. To this, the students responded with humor. "How kind of nature to provide the right conditions for tempering us. This way we will receive the baptism of the revolution."

Nearly all of them developed blisters on their feet. Several had swollen ankles. When they looked at the map to see how far they had come, the distance seemed pitifully small in comparison with the road ahead of them.

So they sat down and opened Chairman Mao's works: "In times of difficulty, we must not lose sight of our achievements, we must see the bright future and pluck up our courage."

The lines in his poem "The Long March" also gave them strength:

The Red Army fears not the trials of a distant march;
To them a thousand mountains, ten thousand rivers are
   nothing.

Another passage they discussed excitedly was Chairman Mao's statement that "The Long March is a manifesto, a propaganda force, a seeding-machine." They commented: "We're also on a long march. We can propagate Mao Tse-tung's thought and sow revolutionary seeds as we go along. We can integrate with the workers and peasants; we can learn from the class feelings and the revolutionary style of veteran workers and former poor peasants. This will be entirely in keeping with Chairman Mao's teachings."

They were convinced that Chairman Mao's heart was with the masses, that more than anyone he supported their revolutionary creativeness, that he would welcome their march to Peking.

Fully confident, they continued their trek.

On August 29, they arrived in Hsiungyueh. At five in the afternoon of August 31, they reached Yingkou, where they learned that Chairman Mao had received five hundred thousand Red Guards and revolutionary teachers and students in Peking earlier that day. They put down their packs and hurried to find a radio, so that they could listen to a transcribed broadcast of the rally.

They smiled delightedly when the cheers and shouts of "Long Live Chairman Mao!" came over the air. Then Comrade Chou En-lai spoke. "At present," he said, "students from various parts of the country are coming to Peking to exchange experience, while students from Peking are going to other places to establish revolutionary ties. We think this is a very good thing. We support you. The Party Central Committee has decided that all college students and representatives from middle-school students in other parts of the country should come to Peking group after group."

The long marchers leapt for joy. Hearing the voice of the Party Central Committee and Chairman Mao was like getting rain after a long period of drought. Their blood raced and their eyes filled with tears as they shouted: "Long live Chairman Mao! Chairman Mao is the red sun in our hearts!"

All their weariness vanished without a trace. Fly on, Long March Red Guards, bold young eagles! Peking is waiting for you! Chairman Mao will be there to welcome you!

TO BE HEROES IN THE FACE OF DIFFICULTIES

Six Branch River flowed steadily towards the Pohai Sea. A ferry plied its broad expanse.

When the Red Guards arrived at the river's edge, they had already been marching for three weeks, and they had that day covered nearly thirty miles. It was twilight. The old boatman, seeing the dusty band with their red banner floating in the wind, immediately knew who they were. He rowed his boat towards the shore, shouting: "Climb aboard! You're in the great Cultural Revolution, so there's no charge."

But the students, inspired by Chairman Mao's swim across the mighty Yangtze earlier that year, were eager to breast the swift current. They had walked a long way, and they were tired. But revolutionaries had to be heroes when they encountered difficulties. Did not Chairman Mao in his poem "Swimming" say:

> I care not that the wind blows and the waves beat;
> It is better than idly strolling in a courtyard.

"In we go! We'll swim across!"

"Swim?" The old boatman was alarmed. "But the water is deep."

"All the better!"

The old man was moved. He could see how tired they were, and he knew the river grew cold after sunset. Besides, it was already well past the swimming season. He tried another tack: "Actually the water is only up to your waist— it's hardly worth swimming. And it's late. Come on, I'll ferry you over and you can get some rest sooner."

The boys thanked him for his good intentions, but their minds were made up. Stripping off their clothes, they plunged into the water. It was icy cold, but their hearts were warm. They were soon across.

In three weeks, they had marched over 300 miles. Most of them suffered badly from blisters and from the sand and gravel that got into their shoes and irritated their aching feet. But Chairman Mao gave them the strength to conquer pain. They read from his *Quotations* and encouraged each other with his words. They kept reminding themselves: "Every step brings us nearer to Peking and Chairman Mao!"

On September 21, they set out in the morning from Yutien County, Hopei Province. They decided to try and reach the county town of Sanho the same night. This meant covering a distance of forty miles—the most they had ever done in a day.

They started at their usual pace. Those whose ankles and feet were sore gritted their teeth and hobbled on.

By nightfall, they were still trudging down the highway that led to Sanho. Some people on bicycles came up and said: "Are you the Long March Red Guards?"

"Yes."

"Hop on. We'll give you a lift into town."

These were students from the East Wind Middle School, who had learned of the red marchers through circulars sent on ahead. Hearing the marchers would pass their village that evening, they had ridden to meet them. But the Red Guards insisted on walking.

Another group of riders met them when they were still two miles from Sanho. These were students from the East Is Red Middle School, who had also been eagerly awaiting their arrival. At the sight of the weary marchers, they were moved beyond words. They hung the boys' packs on their handlebars and urged them to sit on the parcel racks of the bikes.

Gently but firmly the boys replied: "We'd rather walk, thanks."

That's how the Red Guard marchers were. They relied on Mao Tse-tung's thought and their own sturdy legs to complete a trek of 700 miles.

CARRYING ON THE REVOLUTIONARY TRADITIONS

One day, early in September, they had been sleeping the night in a school. In the silence that precedes the dawn, they began to get up. Outside, scattered stars were fading in the vast, dark universe, but the North Star was still steady and bright. We Chinese often compare our great leader, Chairman Mao, to the North Star, for he is the one who shows the road forward.

Eager to continue their march and see Chairman Mao, they shook off their drowsiness and rolled out of bed. By the time the sun had climbed to the rim of the horizon, they had already swept the courtyard and cleaned their quarters. This was a "tradition" of theirs. Wherever they went, whether in the cities or the villages, they were one with the masses, eating, living, and working together with them. And they always left their accommodation neat and clean, and paid to the last penny for what they used.

Soon they were ready to march. They were only waiting for the boy in charge of eating arrangements to return from settling their account. At last he came running back, out of breath and sweating. When they asked what had kept him, he explained:

While they had been at the school, they had consumed nine pounds and nine ounces of grain. The man in charge of the school kitchen accounts had knocked off an ounce and charged them for an even nine and a half pounds. But the marchers had made a vow when they set out that they would scrupulously obey the Three Main Rules of Discipline and the Eight Points for Attention, which Chairman Mao had personally drawn up for the PLA. They were particularly conscious of the clause which read: "Do not take a single needle or a piece of thread from the masses." So the boy had sought out the man in charge and insisted on paying for the extra ounce.

The accountant was moved. His mind flew back to the well-disciplined soldiers he had observed in the War of Liberation. Admiringly, he said: "You boys really have the style of the PLA!"

A SMALL RECTIFICATION MEETING

Wherever the banner of the Long March Red Guards appeared, they were enthusiastically welcomed and treated cordially. When poor and lower-middle peasants heard they were going to see Chairman Mao, they would often dig up sweet potatoes or grind corn meal for them. Once, some workers in a printing press, who had just come off shift, heard that the boys were propagating the Cultural Revolution. They promptly put on their overalls again and went back to work, staying up all night printing leaflets for them. Students in primary and middle schools, when they learned that the boys were going to Peking, would run many miles to meet them, and see them many miles on their way.

They were so often welcomed with drums and cymbals and words of praise that a few of them started getting swelled heads.

One afternoon, they were swinging through the Shanhaikuan Pass, near the eastern end of the Great Wall. Beneath a cloudless sky, the Wall undulated into the distance as far as the eye could see. The boys were impressed yet again with the splendor and magnificence of their land. They were reminded of a poem by Chairman Mao:

The sky is high, the clouds are pale,
We watch the wild geese flying south till they vanish;
We count the myriad leagues we have come already;
If we reach not the Great Wall we are not true men!

They looked at their map and made some calculations. They had completed over half their journey; the worst was over. Some of them grew a trifle complacent.

One day, as they approached a school, they were surprised to find a large poster addressed to them. The ink on it was not yet dry. It read: "If you're really revolutionaries—welcome! If you're not—clear out!"

Some of the marchers were indignant. We've climbed mountains, they thought, forded rivers, dined on the wind, and slept in the dew for the sake of the revolution, and here are people suggesting we're out on a pleasure jaunt! Some were so upset they could not eat.

The cooler heads among them saw this as a sign of incipient pride, of an inability to take the rough with the smooth.

That night they all sat round and opened their *Quotations from Chairman Mao Tse-tung*. They read aloud from the little red books:

To win country-wide victory is only the first step in a long march of ten thousand miles. . . .

Even if we achieve gigantic successes in our work, there is no reason whatever to feel conceited and arrogant. Modesty helps one to go forward, whereas conceit makes one lag behind. This is a truth we must always bear in mind.

In the light of Chairman Mao's teachings, the boys attacked conceit and self-indulgence, exposing the selfishness that often lurks in the depths of people's souls. Everyone took part, and the discussion grew animated.

"We've had too much applause," said one of the boys. "It's gone to our heads."

"We only like to hear compliments; we don't like to hear anything unpleasant."

"We still have a long way to go. We've nothing to be proud of."

"You've got to forget yourself in a revolution. You mustn't be afraid of being misunderstood or treated unfairly. Are we going to quit being revolutionaries just because some people have misunderstood us?"

"That poster has its good side. It's reminded us to stay on our toes, and not to forget that the purpose of our Long March is revolution!"

Public spirit took precedence over private interests, modesty overcame arrogance, determination replaced low spirits. That was the harvest of this small rectification meeting.

The following morning, they took brooms and picks and went out to work. They were not so much trying to change the face of nature as to correct people's impression of them.

Before long, the poster disappeared from the wall. As they proceeded on their way to Peking, revolutionary teachers and students turned out to see them off with applause and smiles.

LEARNING IN SOCIETY

On the vast Liaoho Plain, crops freshened by a rainfall glistened in the sunlight. Like the crops, the Long March Red Guards were thriving. From the rich loam of the lives of workers and peasants, they avidly drew their nourishment. They were learning infinitely more in this way than they could ever have done in a classroom.

One day at noon, they arrived at Tashan Hill and its monument to the martyrs. As the boys recalled the heroic deeds of their revolutionary forbears, they were deeply stirred. Enemy shells had plowed this place into scorched furrows. Now

Tashan was a sea of green, with ripening fruit trees on the hillsides and crops in the fields growing like young trees. The martyrs slept beneath the earth, but a new generation, following in their bloody footprints, was marching along the road of socialist revolution.

Standing before the monument, the Red Guards took a solemn vow that they would carry on the unfinished task of the martyrs and defend a proletarian China to the end of their days.

That's how the Long March Red Guards were—they traveled and learned at the same time. In the small town of Ershihlipu in Chinhsien County, they visited Ma Yu-cheng, a model worker who had been leading the local peasants in a creative study and application of Chairman Mao's works, with the result that they had solved a serious water shortage.

In the past, bourgeois "experts" had proclaimed that this area contained no subsurface water. But after Ma and the local people had read together Chairman Mao's "The Foolish Old Man Who Moved the Mountains," they vowed to find water if they had to dig clear through to the other side of the globe! And find it they did—at a depth of nearly 300 feet. "Bourgeois 'experts' and 'authorities,'" said the local commune leader. "They were really a pack of fat-heads! Old Ma here is a better teacher."

The boys agreed. "People from poor and lower-middle peasant families are the best teachers of all. We should be their students, their children. We must not be successors to the bourgeois professors."

The affectionate guidance they received from workers and peasants swept like a tide through the boys' hearts, cleansing away the stains they had acquired in their academic studies. Their ideology improved day by day.

They had brought a carrying pole with them when they had set out from Talien. At first they had used it to relieve some of the weaker members of part of their loads. Later, all the boys became self-reliant, and the pole was of little use.

Someone even thought it was a bit of an eyesore; it swung awkwardly, and spoiled their appearance when they spruced themselves up and marched into a new town. He suggested throwing it away.

The others disagreed. "If we jettison this carrying pole," they said, "we'll be jettisoning with it the class feelings of the workers and peasants, the style of hard work and bitter struggle. We'll keep it."

During their journey, they developed a simple, hard-working style. They mended their own clothes, patched their own shoes. Their sewing wasn't much good, but they were never ashamed of their handiwork. One boy's shoes were nothing but patches, but he somehow couldn't bear to part with them. This was a complete change from the days when they were in school. Then, they had not been very appreciative of the labors of workers and peasants.

AN OUTSTANDING PROPAGANDA FORCE

The Long March is a manifesto, a propaganda force, a seeding-machine.

In keeping with Chairman Mao's teachings, the Long March Red Guards spread the seeds of Mao Tse-tung's thought wherever they went.

One day they were eating lunch in a busy inn in the town of Nankuan Pass. They felt this would be a good chance to do some propaganda work. So they took from their packs printed quotations from Chairman Mao and big posters in red and green and pasted them on the walls of the inn. People crowded round to read:

Make the Whole Country a Great School of Mao Tse-tung's Thought!
Smash the Old World, Build a New One!

Red Guards writing posters

And many more. At the same time, one of the boys got up on a bench and began reading in a loud voice from his little red book: "Chairman Mao teaches us: 'After the enemy with guns has been wiped out, there will still be enemies without guns; they are bound to struggle desperately against us; and we must never regard these enemies lightly. If we do not now raise and understand the problem in this way, we shall commit the gravest mistakes.'"

The guests stopped eating and gazed approvingly at the boy. A hush fell on the restaurant as they listened to him read from the *Quotations*.

Everywhere they went, they read to the people. The revolutionary masses warmly welcomed this spreading of the thought of Mao Tse-tung. Peasants came miles on bicycles to ask for leaflets.

The boys passed out thousands, for these were revolutionary seeds. Soon, their knapsacks were empty, yet there were many people on the road ahead waiting eagerly for literature. The Red Guards realized they had not brought enough.

They decided to print more immediately. Skimping on food and expenses, they bought some simple mimeograph equipment. This was like a weapon in a good soldier's hands. They cut stencils tirelessly—on peasants' platform beds, on dining-room tables in government-office canteens, beneath feeble lamplight, plagued by mosquitoes far into the night, still they cut. They even made stencils on the march, during breaks. They carved into those stencils their limitless love for Chairman Mao, their infinite respect for his thought. The magnificent determination of the masses of workers and peasants tipped their pens, and with these pens they excoriated the reactionaries. As Chairman Mao's poem put it:

We pointed the finger at our land,
We praised and condemned through our writings,
And those in high positions we counted no more than dust.

At dusk one evening, arriving at a commune brigade head-quarters, they found that everyone was out in the courtyard husking corn. Without a word, they quietly joined the work in the dark.

Gradually they got to chatting with the commune members. Then one of the boys began reading quotations from the little red book by the light of another boy's flashlight.

Animation spread through the courtyard. The peasants were moved by the Red Guards' love for Chairman Mao and his thought, and their tireless devotion to the revolution.

"Your spirit alone is good propaganda," they said. "We'll make you a promise: We guarantee to finish our autumn harvest ahead of schedule."

Some of the boys had difficulty falling asleep that night. They lay there thinking of the ardent devotion of the poor and lower-middle peasants to Chairman Mao, of the deep emotion with which the young commune members had touched their *Quotations from Chairman Mao Tse-tung*. They knew the peasants were too busy in this season to go to town much and had not been able to buy many copies of the book. They decided to donate two of their own copies to the brigade.

The sky was getting light and they had to be on their way. They placed two little red books in the hands of the Communist Party secretary, who accepted them with tears in his eyes, unable to speak for emotion. He could only wave the gleaming red volumes in farewell, as the Long March Red Guards flew on toward Peking.

BEFORE US IS

AN AGE OF SPRING

[The Cultural Revolution lasted three years. To some Americans, that might seem a long time to be absorbed in political activities. To Americans who have participated in the civil rights or antiwar movements, it might seem a comparatively short and successful campaign.

The fortunes of the Chinese students fluctuated wildly during those three years. At times, it seemed that they were running the movement; at other times—particularly toward the end, they were subordinate to workers, peasants, and Liberation Army soldiers. Now, in 1971, the schools and colleges are back in operation, but many of the former students have gone out to work in factories or in the countryside. Needless to add, the education system will never be quite the same again.

China's political system will never be the same, either. The Party has lost much of its prestige; Red Guard leaders have entered the power structure; the army has gained in stature. China is now run—at every level—by committees made up of these three elements in varying proportions. This is a big change in a country where the Communist Party was previously unchallenged.

We in the West have not caught up with what happened in 1949 yet. Nor do we understand the China of the 1950's. Now the Chinese have pushed on into "the era of Mao Tse-tung's thought" while we still flounder in questions that are twenty years old: "Should China be admitted to the United Nations?" "What about Taiwan?" "Are the Chinese aggressive?" "Are they more Chinese than communist, or more communist than Chinese?"

It is the responsibility of young Americans to do what their elders have failed so miserably to do: to sympathize with China, to understand what she has done and what she is trying to do, to see whether solutions that she has sought to her problems might in any way be applicable to some of our problems in the West. Bureaucratism, technocracy, professional irresponsibility, elitism, urbanization, over-centralized authority, the restriction or denial of power that should belong to the people—these are presumably not only China's problems.

This book has been designed to give young Americans a chance to listen to some voices from China—particularly to the voices of *young* Chinese. It would seem appropriate, therefore, to end with a poem by young Chinese —Red Guards from the Kaifeng Normal School.

The poem—published in 1967—is not typical of modern Chinese literature as a whole; nor is it especially elegant artistically. It is arrogant in parts; it is dogmatic in parts. It has the faults of a very young and very proud culture that has risen from the ashes of a very old and very proud culture.

Its main quality—and it is an authentic Chinese quality—is its supreme optimism. It is the work of youngsters who are utterly convinced that no force on earth can stop the world's people—and that means the world's *poor* people—from setting themselves free from oppression.

Its enthusiasm is so tangible that it frightens us, and we want to dismiss it as childish. Like most Chinese literature, it is worth reading two or three times, to make sure it is the voices from China that are garbled, and not something in ourselves that stops our hearing.]

The Five Continents and the Four Seas
Are illumined by the radiance
Of Mao Tse-tung's thought!

毛主席说：我们的文学艺术都是为人民大众的，首先是为工农兵的，为工农兵而創作，为工农兵所利用的。 《在延安文艺座谈会上的讲话》

At the bottom of the poster: "Chairman Mao says, 'All our literature and art are for the masses of the people, and in the first place for the workers, peasants, and soldiers; they are created for the workers, peasants, and soldiers and are for their use.'"

The calendar of the new year
Opens to the storm
Of the great Cultural Revolution!

This last year
With the hot blood
And the sweat of our youth
We have painted
Rich colors
On the canvas of this age.

The hard work of the men of Taching
Has sent oil rushing
To the factories and farms;
The self-reliance of the men of Tachai
Has raised their terraced fields
To the clouds!

Red, red mushroom clouds
Have blossomed
High in the sky;
Each fresh wave
Of the big Leap Forward
Swirling higher than the last!

The whole wide world
Will be transmuted
Into purest crimson
By the fierce flames
Of the Cultural Revolution
Kindled by Chairman Mao!

Ghosts and monsters
Will be crushed
To pieces;

For the old world
Must be totally overthrown—
Smashed beyond recognition.

The reactionary bourgeois line,
Like leaves falling in the west wind,
Has bitten the dust:
Now, like the rising sun,
The proletarian revolutionary line
Sings a song of triumph!

As the drums roll
We greet the great victories
Of Mao Tse-tung's thought;
Amidst red flowers
We welcome the coming
Of nineteen sixty-seven.

A red-hot energy
Seethes in the veins
Of the Chinese people!
Their hearts
Thrill and throb
With revolutionary passion!

Listen! Drums roll,
And before us
Is the spring of a new age.
Look! Red flags flutter!
Before us
Is an age of spring!

Quick!
Fill the tanks of all the generators
With the oil of Taching.

Quick!
Sow the whole countryside
With seeds from Tachai!

Plumper ears of grain
Will grow in the heat
From Chairman Mao's words;
The motor
Of the Cultural Revolution
Will speed up every lathe!

Let every inch of soil
Bespeak the firm resolve
Of the poor and lower-middle peasants;
Let every workshop
Display the revolutionary spirit
Of the working class.

Oh, comrades-in-arms,
Make haste to use the iron brush
Given us by our class;
Seething with hatred
Let us scour away the filth
Of the bourgeois reactionary line!

Comrades, oh, comrades!
Quickly unroll the scroll of paper
Given us by the age;
With fiery ardor
Let us paint our boundless love
For the Party and Chairman Mao!

"Do not say that the strong pass
Is guarded with iron. This very day
In one step we shall pass its summit."

We complete our "Long March"
In one stride, and trample underfoot
Ten thousand soaring peaks!

Each day a new beginning,
Each new beginning
A song of triumph!
Each step a footprint;
From each footprint
Springs a clump of flowers!

Ah, our age
Is as young as the morning,
As red as the heart of a fire!
Forward!
It is we who steer the universe,
The future is ours!

Let the radiance
Of Mao Tse-tung's thought
Shine forever above this earth!
Surely the future of mankind
Will be lived
In the world of the red flag.

A CHRONOLOGY OF CHINESE HISTORY

21st century B.C.—17th century B.C. The *Hsia*, first of a long line of ruling houses, or dynasties.

17th century B.C.—11th century B.C. The *Shang* Dynasty.

11th century B.C.—221 B.C. The *Chou* Dynasty, or classical period of Chinese antiquity. After 771 B.C., the *Chou* rulers had less and less real power. The breakdown of the centralized empire gave rise to a long philosophical debate between rival schools, each offering solutions to the social ills of the time. The *Warring States* period (476 B.C.–221 B.C.) saw the debate carried to the battlefield, as the fragments of the empire fought for supremacy.

221 B.C. The *Ch'in* state conquered the last of its rivals and unified the empire.

206 B.C.–A.D. 220. The *Han* Dynasty. This was a period of relative peace, during which the Confucianists gained supremacy in social and ideological matters.

A.D. 220–581. Under repeated "barbarian" invasions, the empire again disintegrated. For a time, *Three Kingdoms* strove for power. Later, the realm was divided into northern and southern areas. Finally, the *Sui* Dynasty (A.D. 581–618) reunited the empire by force.

A.D. 618–907. The *T'ang* Dynasty. This was another long period of prosperity, during which Chinese classical culture is said to have reached its peak.

A.D. 907–960. The *Five Dynasties*. More division occurred in this period.

A.D. 960–1279. The *Sung* Dynasty. There was unity under its stable rule.

1279–1368. The Mongols invaded and ruled China. This was the time of Marco Polo's visit.

1368–1644. The *Ming* Dynasty drove out the Mongols and ruled for three centuries.

1644–1911. The Manchus conquered China and set up the *Ch'ing*

Dynasty. The arrival of the Europeans in the nineteenth century accelerated its decline. Great uprisings like the Taiping Rebellion (1850's and 1860's) and the Boxer Movement (1900) preceded the downfall of the Manchus.

1911. The revolution led by Dr. Sun Yat-sen overthrew the empire.

1912–26. Warlords fought for power.

1919. Students demonstrated in Peking against the post–World War I transfer of Shantung province from Germany to Japan.

1920. The Communist Party of China was founded.

1922–27. The Communist Party and the Kuomintang (Nationalist Party) cooperated in a united front.

1926. Chiang Kai-shek led the Northern Expedition to reunite the country.

1927. A massacre of Communists was instigated by the Kuomintang. Mao led a band of troops to Chingkangshan to wage guerrilla war.

1930–34. Mao's men repelled four Kuomintang attacks on their mountain base.

1931. Japan invaded Manchuria.

1932. Japan bombed Shanghai.

1934–35. Mao's forces were compelled to make the Long March.

1935. Mao was elected Chairman of the Communist Party.

1936. The Communists made their base at Yenan in the northwest. Chiang Kai-shek was kidnapped by warlord allies but was released owing to the good offices of Chou En-lai.

1937. Full-scale war broke out between Japan and China.

1945. Japan was defeated.

1946–49. Civil war was fought between the Communists and the Nationalists.

1949. Chiang Kai-shek fled to Taiwan. Mao proclaimed the People's Republic of China.

1950. The Korean War broke out.

1958. The Great Leap Forward. People's Communes were established.

1959–62. The "Three Lean Years."

1966–69. The Great Proletarian Cultural Revolution.

SUGGESTIONS FOR FURTHER READING

CH'EN, JEROME. *Mao and the Chinese Revolution.* New York and London: Oxford University Press, 1965. The story of Mao's life is skillfully woven into the history of modern China. Translations of thirty-seven of Mao's poems are included.

China Pictorial. China Reconstructs. Chinese Literature. Monthly magazines from Peking. A rich, though somewhat idealized, source of photos, articles, and fiction about China.

FITZGERALD, C. P. *China: A Short Cultural History.* 3d ed. New York: Praeger, 1961. One of the best general surveys of Chinese history available.

HAN SUYIN. *China in the Year 2001.* New York: Basic Books, 1967. A survey of the unique qualities of Chinese society and how they will affect China's development. The author, daughter of a Chinese father and a Belgian mother, has also written a fascinating autobiography in three volumes: *The Crippled Tree, A Mortal Flower,* and *Birdless Summer.*

HINTON, WILLIAM. *Fanshen.* London: Monthly Review Press, 1967. An American farmer who experienced the Chinese revolution at first hand records his impressions.

HUNTER, NEALE. *Shanghai Journal: An Eyewitness Account of the Cultural Revolution.* New York: Praeger, 1969. Neale Hunter's account of what he saw and read during the first year of this important movement.

LIN YI. *A Short History of China, 1840–1919.* Peking: Foreign Languages Press, 1963. The impact of Western imperialism, judged from a Chinese perspective.

LU HSÜN. *Selected Works.* Peking: Foreign Languages Press, 1956. Four volumes of stories and essays by a master of satire and the most influential writer of pre-Communist China.

MAO TSE-TUNG. *Selected Works.* Peking: Foreign Languages Press, 1967. Far and away the most important primary source for an understanding of modern China. The "Three Old Favorites" are included here, as are such key articles as "Report on an Investigation into the Peasant Movement in Hunan," "Talks at the Yenan Forum on Art and Literature," "Farewell, Leighton Stuart!," and many others.

SNOW, EDGAR. *Red Star over China.* New York: Grove Press, 1968. Perhaps the most exciting book on China ever written—certainly the most exciting by an American. A classical eyewitness account of the revolution in the 1930's, including personal interviews with Mao Tse-tung and other Communist leaders.

SNOW, EDGAR. *The Other Side of the River.* New York: Random House, 1962. Twenty-five years after *Red Star over China,* the author returns to see the new society. A voluminous record of his impressions.

INDEX